CREATIVE PHOTOGRAPHY

1826 TO THE PRESENT

an exhibition from
The Gernsheim Collection

by Helmut and Alison Gernsheim

Detroit, 1963
WAYNE STATE UNIVERSITY PRESS

CREATIVE PHOTOGRAPHY
1826 TO THE PRESENT
an exhibition from the Gernsheim Collection

Previous showings of this exhibition:

Victoria and Albert Museum, London. May-October 1951. Special Festival of Britain exhibition under the auspices of the Arts Council of Great Britain.

World Exhibition of Photography, Art Museum, Lucerne, Switzerland. May-August 1952.

Art Museum, Gothenburg, Sweden. April-June 1956.

Fodor Museum (Stedelijk Museum), Amsterdam, Holland. July-August 1956.

Nordisk Museum, Stockholm, Sweden. March-June 1957.

11th Triennale, Palazzo dell'Arte, Milan, Italy. August-November 1957.

Folkwang Museum, Essen, Germany. March-May 1959.

Wallraf-Richartz Museum, Cologne, Germany. June-August 1959.

City Art Gallery, Frankfurt, Germany. April-May 1960.

City Museum, Munich, Germany. May-June 1961.

Smaller selections from the Gernsheim Collection:

The Museum of Modern Art, New York, 1950. Photographs by Lewis Carroll.

George Eastman House, Rochester, New York, 1951. Photographs by Lewis Carroll.

City Art Museum, Bournemouth, England. As part of their Festival of Britain exhibition, 1951.

The main cities of England and Scotland under the auspices of the Arts Council of Great Britain. During 1952-53.

"Elizabeth to Elizabeth Exhibition," Stratford House, London. December 1953.

Rome, Florence, Bologna and Milan. 1954. Under the auspices of the British Council.

City Art Gallery, Newcastle on Tyne, England. 1960.

Bibliotheque Nationale, Paris. "Salon du Portrait." December 1960.

County Museum, Warwick, England. July-August 1961. "Portraits of 19th century celebrities."

The approximately 700 photographs in this retrospective exhibition afford the most comprehensive survey ever arranged of artistic photography from its origin to the present day. Alongside unique *incunabula* of the inventors — Niépce, Daguerre, Talbot — can be seen a selection of outstanding pictures by leading photographers of all periods and many countries. Visitors familiar with the subject will have an opportunity to see the originals of many classics they so far know only from reproductions. Many less publicized pictures are, nevertheless, also masterpieces — gems which we rescued from oblivion and which form important links in the evolution of photography as an art.

Owing to the circumstance that photography grew up during a period of rapidly improving transport and communications, its division into national schools as in painting never arose. On the contrary, the evolution of photography is best seen in the styles of each period, which, through the medium of international magazines, have a tendency to lose their national idiom almost overnight.

In the selection of the pictures we have placed the main emphasis on the first century following the official introduction of photography in 1839, on account of the greater rarity and novelty of the earlier period. Nevertheless, the pioneers of modern photography — those who opened up new fields or explored new ways of expression — are shown with representative and frequently famous works. Most leading contemporary photographers are active in the field of documentation and reportage, depicting the face of our time. Adequate coverage of modern photography would require an exhibition of its own.

While the miniature camera and fast films make it possible to seize dramatic moments which eluded the cumbersome apparatus of earlier decades, the photographic visualization of momentous events in the nineteenth-century reportages found expression in outstanding pictures which are an inspiration and a challenge to modern photographers. A study of the first war reportage by Roger Fenton, and of the first social documentation by John Thomson, will convey better than words the superlative quality they achieved in 1855 and 1876 respectively.

Technical evolution is represented by a varied selection of apparatus, beginning with a scioptric ball of the mid-seventeenth century and *camera obscuras* and *camera lucidas* of the 18th and early 19th centuries, which were extensively used as an aid in drawing long before the invention of the photographic camera. Examples of photographic apparatus typical of each period afford a better understanding of the technical difficulties photographers had to contend with before factory-produced sensitive materials, miniature cameras, and enlarging made photography the most popular pastime of the 20th century.

Those who believe 3D to be an invention of our time will be surprised at the array of stereoscopic viewers dating back to the mid-1850's, which gave our forebears as much entertainment as television gives us. The same applies to the zoetrope and numerous other instruments once regarded as amusing and instructive toys, but today avidly collected by experts as forerunners of cinematography.

The pre-history of photography in optics and in chemistry is covered by all important publications on the subject, going back to the first published description of the *camera obscura* by a pupil of Leonardo da Vinci (1521), and Schulze's report on his photo-chemical researches (1727) which eventually led Wedgwood to make the first attempts at photography around 1800.

Among many unique treasures seen for the first time outside Europe none will arouse greater interest than the various exhibits by Nicéphore Niépce: the two manuscripts on Heliography, with which he tried in 1827 to interest King George IV of England and the Royal Society, London, in his invention; the first photograph from nature; and the equally renowned photo-engraving of Cardinal d'Amboise. With these Niépce laid the foundation stone of photography and of photomechanical reproduction. In our daily life we take for granted photographic reproductions in books, newspapers and magazines, yet until satisfactory photo-mechanical printing processes had been developed, the only way of illustrating books and magazines with photographs was to stick original prints between or on the text pages. Editions were of necessity small. The *incunabula* in this field are Talbot's "The Pencil of Nature" (1844) and "Sun Pictures in Scotland" (1845). They were followed by a comparatively small number of English, French, German and American publications before 1870, which are now rare.

*   *   *   *   *

In 1826, twenty-eight years after Senefelder's invention of lithography, Nicéphore Niépce, a French landowner, succeeded in recording the image of the *camera obscura* on a sensitized pewter plate. Lacking skill in drawing, Niépce tried to fix the *camera obscura* pictures on lithographic stone, and thus he was led to the invention of photography. This circumstance established a link between two techniques which had to struggle for recognition as artistic media for over a hundred years.

The daguerreotype, which was a modification and perfection of Niépce's Heliography, was a mirror of nature. In 1845 Ruskin compared a daguerreotype of Venice with a painting by Canaletto of the same building, and gave preference to the finely detailed photograph. Ingres admitted, looking at a daguerreotype portrait: "It is to this exactitude that I would like to attain: it is wonderful — but one must not say so." Perhaps better known than any other opinion of an artist is Paul Delaroche's exclamation of bewilderment on first seeing a daguerreotype: "From today, painting is dead!" It is true that the functions of representational painting were eventually taken over by photography, but at first it was chiefly portraiture that suffered, until the constantly widening scope of photography released painting from representation altogether.

In the early period it did not occur to photographers to deviate from the straightforward recording of the world around them which is the true function of photography. It was recognized that photography had certain limitations in subject matter, yet despite these it offered sufficient scope for artistic expression. However, the annual exhibitions of the Photographic Society of London, which from 1854 onward aroused great interest, caused art critics to draw comparisons between photography and painting, and to spur on photographers to "higher ideals" than the "mere reproduction" of objects. Photographs of historical, allegorical, literary or anecdotal content, similar to academic painting of the period, were the best way—so the critics believed—to overcome the reproach that photography was a mechanical art. Some photographers, too, who had formerly been artists, failed to appreciate that such painterly subject matter was totally unsuitable for the realistic representation inherent in the new technique. Incongruous "fine art" compositions resulted from this mistaken ambition to emulate painting, which sometimes affected even the greatest photographers of the nineteenth century, David Octavius Hill and Julia Margaret Cameron, whose splendid portraits of the great Victorians are unsurpassed.

Although the first generation of photographers remained true to photographic technique, around the turn of the century there started a craze for controlled printing processes such as bromoil and gum prints, which enabled the photographer to give his picture the appearance of a chalk or charcoal drawing or of a reproduction of an oil painting. This tempted many photographers to demonstrate their skill by manual interference with the photographic image. The more the original photograph disappeared in this metamorphosis, the higher was the praise bestowed by art critics. One wrote in 1898: "Photographers have broken the tradition of the artificial reproduction of Nature. They have freed themselves from photography. They have done away with photographic sharpness, the clear and disturbing representation of details, and can achieve simple, broad effects." And so it came about that in 1899 photographs were hung in the Royal Academy, Berlin, a year after the Munich and Vienna Secessions had opened their doors to photography.

A reaction against this decadent style of Salon photography during the *art nouveau* period started in New York with the work of Alfred Stieglitz, who stressed that photography and painting are fundamentally different media, that each has its own functions and has to go its separate way. Already in the mid-1880's, P. H. Emerson had warned against the artificialities of the "fine art" photographers of the H. P. Robinson school, and became the founder of Naturalistic Photography. Now, at the turn of the century, Stieglitz pioneered a new outlook, urging photographers to take their hand cameras out to record everyday life and activities — yet such subjects were frowned upon by art photographers as "inartistic record work." Fortunately the majority of the great photographers remained unaffected by the stifling atmosphere of societies and clubs, and in retrospect it is the independents who carried the day, and who are chiefly represented in this exhibition. There is nothing artificial or arty about their work; they remained true to their medium, its function and limitations, and did not prostitute their art for the sake of winning medals.

A surprisingly large number of leading nineteenth-century photographers were amateurs who could afford to please themselves. Professionals chiefly took portraits, and were satisfied if their business prospered. It is curious that many famous photographers were active for only a few years; sometimes photography was just a sideline to them. D. O. Hill was a painter, Dr. Keith a surgeon, Bayard a civil servant, Fenton a trial advocate, Carjat a caricaturist, Adam-Salomon a sculptor, Lewis Carroll an author, Emerson a doctor, Julia Margaret Cameron a member of aristocratic intellectual society, etc.

The documentary and reportage approach of photographers like Thomson, Riis, Hine, Strand and Atget came into its own only after World War I, when the old painterly tradition was finally swept away — in painting as well as in photography — and new ways were sought for artistic expression.

The greatest impact on modern photography came from Germany in the 1920's. At the Bauhaus, Moholy-Nagy experimented with abstract patterns; Renger-Patzsch became the exponent of "New Objectivity"; and Erich Salomon pioneered modern reportage by available light. There were also other exponents of these new ideas, some trying to align photography to modern art, others to bring it back to its original purity. The brutal realism of Eisenstein's "Battleship Potemkin" and Pabst's "Joyless Street" expressed this tendency in the cinema, and there is no doubt that they left their mark on still photography. The classic rules of composition and perspective laid down for painting in the Renaissance were now deliberately discarded, and photographers gradually learned to *see photographically;* i.e., to follow the natural laws of vision, which seemed also the most suitable for the camera's eye at a time when it could truly be said: "What you can see, you can photograph." The wide-aperture lenses constructed in Germany in the mid-twenties, in conjunction with small plate and miniature cameras, played their part in extending the boundaries of photography.

Parallel to New Objectivity yet, despite similar aims, independent of it, the F 64 Group was founded in California by Edward Weston in 1932. Shortly afterwards Cartier-Bresson and Brassaï in France, and a team of photographers working for the Farm Security Administration in the United States, brought to documentation and reportage a candidness which at first shocked by its starkness, but was soon recognized as the legitimate commentary of socially conscious observers on the misdeeds of our time. In depicting conditions of life objectively, photography had found its most important function.

*   *   *   *   *

In the comparatively short span of time since Niépce took the first photograph in 1826, photography has become so indispensable in our civilization that leading scientists have called it "the most important invention since that of the printing-press." But a similar recognition of photography as an *art form* has not yet been so generally accorded to it. This is, however, only a matter of time. Already during recent years some important photographic exhibitions, including Steichen's "Family of Man" and the present show, have convinced progressive art critics and museum directors that the old concept denying photography the status of art needs drastic revision.

Several art institutions and universities in the United States have for years accepted photography as one of the arts and done valuable work in furthering photography as an art form. Pioneer in this field was Beaumont Newhall, who in 1937 arranged the first retrospective show of photography in modern times. Both at the Museum of Modern Art and later at George Eastman House, Rochester, Mr. and Mrs. Newhall have furthered the appreciation of the Old Masters of photography and extended recognition to contemporary work. For someone as keenly interested in the history and aesthetics of photography as Helmut Gernsheim, Beaumont Newhall's suggestion, made during a visit to London in January 1945, to rescue and preserve for posterity what had not already been destroyed by neglect or war damage, fell on fertile ground. From small beginnings while V2 rockets were falling on London, the Gernsheim Collection grew by leaps and bounds. It was evident to us from the very beginning that parallel with the collecting of works of the first importance which must form the core of any great collection, must go intensive study of what was practically virgin ground. A practical division of labor evolved naturally from personal inclinations: Helmut Gernsheim searching for, and Alison Gernsheim researching on, the items. Research in turn necessitated the building up of a specialized library, which today ranks as one of the largest of its kind and probably the richest in rare publications of the 16th to 19th centuries inclusive.

At the time of our first exhibition, "Masterpieces of Victorian Photography," in 1951, we publicly stated our aim: the foundation of a Museum of Photography, to which we would present our collection. It had grown too big for our apartment and needed not only premises of its own, but also staff, and finance to support the cultural and educational program which we envisaged. These facilities were not forthcoming, and we have been forced to carry the burden on our own shoulders to this day. We never wavered, however, from the goal we had set ourselves; to further the appreciation of photography by exhibitions, publications, and lectures. It was a tribute to the high artistic quality of our collection that art museums of international stature opened their doors to a photographic exhibition for the first time in the present century. Our first exihibition was a special Festival of Britain show sponsored by the Arts Council of Great Britain and displayed at the Victoria & Albert Museum, London. Greatly enlarged and international in scope, the exhibition was shown from time to time during the following eleven years in leading art museums of Sweden, Holland, Germany, Switzerland, and Italy, under the title, "A Century of Photography" (later extended to "120 Years of Photography"). It was the first photographic exhibition ever shown at the Triennale in Milan, and has been seen by about 1½ million people. In addition a number of smaller exhibitions from the Gernsheim Collection have been arranged, and we have been told again and again that these shows acted as an eye-opener to art critics and public alike as to the value of photography's contribution to art and civilization.

Though many requests for traveling exhibitions and films for schools had to be refused owing to lack of staff, we reached millions of people by television and radio. Our comprehensive *History of Photography* and a number of other standard works on great nineteenth-century photographers have resulted from our researches. We have also contributed over 150 articles to photographic periodicals and magazines of art, science, and literature. In addition, Helmut Gernsheim has been active as lecturer and exhibition judge.

In digging up the past, our most important finds were the re-discovery of the photographic *opus* of Lewis Carroll, and the world's first photograph by Nicéphore Niépce. Both were widely publicized in the world's press in 1950 and 1952 respectively. Neither was a lucky find, but followed years of intensive research.

Thus, despite the fact that as private individuals we lacked any form of subsidy or outside assistance, we have achieved a good deal of our program, and eighteen years after its foundation the Gernsheim Collection ranks as the most important photo-historical collection in existence.

Owing to the considerable expense involved in bringing the exhibition material to the United States, it was not easy to find sponsors for it in America. The enterprise, which a number of American museums and universities found too great, was carried out by munificent private sponsorship after the appearance of an article about the Gernsheim Collection in *The Detroit News.* To Mrs. Mildred Puddington and Mr. Paul Lansat, the initiators of this exhibition, and to all those who have assisted us in every stage in preparing it, we express our sincere gratitude.

Helmut and Alison Gernsheim.
Detroit, March 1963.

MILESTONES ON THE WAY TO PHOTOGRAPHY

(a) Camera Obscura

1 Vitruvius

De architectura libri dece. Como 1521. First Italian translation from the Latin, edited and with explanations by Cesare Cesariano, a pupil of Leonardo da Vinci. Book I, leaf 23 *verso* contains the first published description of the *camera obscura.*

2 Gemma Frisius

De radio astronomico et geometrico liber. First edition, Antwerp and Louvain 1545. Contains the first published illustration of the *camera obscura*, which until about 1620 was literally a darkened room in a house, with a small hole in the window-shutter through which the landscape or street scene outside was projected onto the opposite wall, or a white screen. In a *camera obscura* with a hole in the skylight the projected image of a solar eclipse could be observed without harming the eyes.

3 Girolamo Cardano

De subtilitate libri XXI. Lyons 1554. In this enlarged edition which appeared four years after the first, Cardano describes a *camera obscura* with a bi-convex lens fitted in the hole—a great improvement which gave brighter and sharper images.

4 Giovanni Battista della Porta

Magiae Naturalis libri IV. Antwerp 1560. Porta's book, which first appeared two years earlier in Naples, contains a long description of the *camera obscura* (without a lens) and its various uses, especially as an aid to art-
ists. Numerous editions and translations of "Magiae Naturalis" in various languages made the principle of the *camera obscura* widely known, and for this reason its invention is often wrongly ascribed to Porta. The edition exhibited is one of the first books published by Christophe Plantin.

5 Daniello Barbaro

La pratica della perspettiva. Venice 1569. Reprint of the first edition of 1568. Barbaro improved the *camera obscura* image by adding diaphragms of various sizes behind the lens.

6 Egnatio Danti

La prospettiva di Euclide. First edition, Florence 1573. Danti made a further improvement in the *camera obscura* by adding a mirror to invert the image, which up to this time had been upside down.

7 Giovanni Battista della Porta

Magiae naturalis libri XX. First edition, Naples 1589. In this enlarged edition in twenty books, Porta mentioned various improvements which had meanwhile been made by Cardano (bi-convex lens), Barbaro (diaphragm) and Danti (reversal of the image by a mirror), implying that these improvements were his own. In this edition the *camera obscura* is for the first time recommended as an aid for artists.

8 Daniel Schwenter

Deliciae Physico-Mathematicae. First edition, Nürnberg 1636. Disseminating previously known information on the *camera obscura*, Schwenter is the first to describe and illustrate the scioptic ball (No. 24), a lens system inserted in the window-shutter.

9 Athanasius Kircher

Ars magna lucis et umbrae. First edition, Rome 1646. Kircher published for the first time an illustration of a portable *camera obscura* which made possible the sketching of landscapes in the open air.

10 Sir Henry Wotton

Reliquiae Wottonianae. First edition, London 1651. First description of a portable tent *camera obscura*, which the astronomer, Johann Kepler, constructed before 1620 as an aid in making topographical drawings.

11 Johann Christoph Sturm

Collegium Experimentale. First edition, Nürnberg 1676. Contains first illustration of a portable reflex *camera obscura*.

12 Johann Zahn

Oculus artificialis Teledioptricus. First edition, Würzburg 1685-86. Kaspar Schott and Johann Christoph Sturm had already described small box and reflex cameras, but Zahn's explanations and illustrations of various types and lens constructions spread the knowledge of these "hand cameras," which underwent no further improvement until the photographic camera, though during the eighteenth century, when the use of the *camera obscura* was widespread, various novel forms were introduced.

13 G. J. 's Gravesande

Usage de la chambre obscure pour le dessein. First edition, The Hague 1711. Describes and illustrates a *camera obscura* in the form of a sedan chair.

14 William Cheselden

The Anatomy of the Human Body. London 1750. Cheselden in 1733 first applied the *camera obscura* (as illustrated on the title-page of this book) as an aid in anatomical drawing.

15 Abbé Nollet

Leçons de physique experimentale. Vol. 5, Paris 1765. Illustrates a tent-type *camera obscura*, and other forms.

16 Edmé-Gilles Guyot

Nouvelles récréations physiques et mathématiques. Vol. III. First edition, Paris 1769-70. Illustrates for the first time a table *camera obscura*.

17 Joseph Harris

A Treatise of Optics. First edition, London 1775. Describes various novel forms of *camera obscura*, including the book camera, the pocket camera, and the walking-stick camera.

(b) Photochemical Researches

18 Johann Heinrich Schulze

"Scotophorus pro Phosphoro Inventus," contained in *Acta physico-medica Academiae Caesariae*, Vol I, Nürnberg 1727. First description of the production of light-images on a mixture of silver nitrate and chalk contained in a bottle, partly protected from light by paper stencils. Schulze was the first to recognize that the darkening of the silver salt was due to sunlight and not to heat or air.

19 William Lewis

Commercium Philosophico-Technicum, or, the Philosophical Commerce of Arts, designed as an Attempt to Improve Arts, Trades and Manufactures. London 1765. The first English book to describe Schulze's experiments, which the author repeated and extended, applying silver nitrate also to solid substances such as white bone, ivory, wood and stone. Dr. Lewis forms a bridge between Schulze and Thomas Wedgwood, whose tutor, Alexander Chisholm, had been Lewis' laboratory assistant.

20 Carl Wilhelm Scheele

Chemical Observations and Experiments on Air and Fire. First English edition, London 1780. Scheele proved that the violet rays of the solar spectrum have a more rapid darkening effect on silver chloride than the other wave-lengths. This fact was a disadvantage in photography until the introduction of panchromatic emulsions in 1906 as it caused an incorrect translation of the colors of nature into the black-and-white tone scale. Scheele also stated that silver chloride acted on by light is no longer soluble in ammonia as the unaffected silver chloride is. This observation would have provided a photographic fixing agent.

21   Jean Senebier

Memoires physico-chymiques sur l'influence de la lumière solaire. First edition, Geneva 1782. Vol. III contains Senebier's photometric investigations on the relative speed with which the different spectrum colors darken silver chloride; and also the hardening effect of light on certain resins.

22   Thomas Wedgwood and Sir Humphry Davy

"An account of a method of copying paintings-upon-glass and of making profiles by the agency of light upon nitrate of silver," contained in Nicholson's *Journal of Natural Philosophy*, Vol. III, London, November 1802. Wedgwood was the first to combine the known photochemical and optical knowledge in a deliberate attempt at photography. He copied paintings-on-glass similar to No. 37, leaves, feathers and other flat objects by superposition on light-sensitive material, and also attempted to fix the images of the *camera obscura* by chemical means, but he and Davy failed to find a method of rendering them permanent, although Scheele had mentioned that silver chloride darkened by light becomes insoluble in ammonia.

23   Sir John Herschel

"On the Hyposulphurous Acid and Its Compounds," contained in *The Edinburgh Philosophical Journal*, Vol. 1, Edinburgh, January 1819. In this paper Herschel published the property of the hyposulphites of soda as a solvent for silver salts. This discovery later became of the greatest importance in photography, for sodium thiosulphate ("hypo") still remains the most widely used fixer.

THE CAMERA OBSCURA AND OTHER OPTICAL AIDS FOR ARTISTS

24   Scioptic ball or "ox-eye" c. 1650

Probably English. A lens system combining three different focal lengths. The front and back lens are each of different focal length; when used together, both give a shorter focus than either separately. When this hollow, revolvable wooden ball, containing the lens system, is screwed into the window-shutter of a darkened room, it projects on the opposite white wall or screen, upright pictures from all directions in which the ball is turned, instead of only the view directly in front of the window. The "ox-eye" was first described and illustrated by Daniel Schwenter in *Deliciae physico-mathematicae*, Nürnberg 1636 (See No. 8). He mentioned that the artist Hans Hauer had used the instrument for drawing a large panoramic view of the city of Nürnberg, and obtained excellent perspective with its aid.

25   Portable reflex camera obscura c. 1750

Constructed by W. & S. Jones, London. When folded up the height is only 14.5 cm, width 30 cm, length 40 cm (5¾″ x 10¾″ x 15¾″). The camera has two lenses; one for portraits and still-life, the other for views. A mirror in the periscope reflects the picture onto a piece of drawing paper at the bottom of the box. The artist observes the picture through a wadded opening in the side of the camera, and inserts his hand through a light-tight sleeve. It is known that Canaletto, Guardi, Crespi of Bologna, Vermeer, and many other artists used the *camera obscura* to make drawings in correct perspective.

26   Reflex box camera obscura c. 1810

Height 11 cm, width 13.5 cm, length 25.5 cm (4½″ x 5¼″ x 10″). A mirror reflects the image onto a ground glass as in a modern reflex camera. A hinged lid with side flaps shades the image while tracing it on transparent paper. Focusing is done by moving the inner box containing the lens, which slides within the outer box. Even a screw-in lens cap was provided. This kind of camera was first described by Johann Zahn in 1685 (see No. 12), and is the type used by Daguerre and Talbot, which gave them the idea of fixing the *camera obscura* images chemically.

27 Claude glass c. 1780

4¾" x 6¼" oval. A convex mirror of black glass, named after the famous French painter Claude Lorraine who is supposed to have made use of such a glass three centuries ago as an aid in composition. Claude glasses were extensively used by eighteenth-century painters, and the device retained its usefulness for nineteenth-century photographers as it shows how a view will look when reduced, and, to some extent, when reproduced in monochrome, for the black glass largely eliminates color.

28 Camera lucida c. 1830

Produced by Watkins & Hill, London. Length 8¾", when fully extended 50 cm 19¾". This optical aid for drawing, invented by W. H. Wollaston in 1807, was called by him *camera lucida,* because the image appears, not in a dark box, but by full daylight. ("Camera" is, of course, an incorrect term.) Actually it is only a virtual image which the artist sees through the "sight" over the four-sided prism and one of the two lenses (for long or short sight) apparently reflected on the paper. Like its precursor the *camera obscura,* the *camera lucida* was used by professional and amateur artists. It found widespread application especially in England and France, following the publication in 1829 of Capt. Basil Hall's book, "40 Etchings from Sketches made with the *camera lucida* in North America in 1827 and 1828." In 1833 Talbot tried the *camera lucida,* but not being a skillful sketcher found the *camera obscura* easier to use.

29 Camera lucida c. 1830

Made by G. Dollond, London. 8" long, with extensions, and four additional lenses. In original case. Capt. Basil Hall found it useful to have a variety of lenses to correct the parallax according to the distance of the subject.

30 *Description of the camera lucida, an instrument for drawing in true perspective, and for copying, reducing, or enlarging other drawings. With a letter on the use of the camera, by Capt. Basil Hall.* London 1830.

31 Instruction leaflet for No. 28.

FORERUNNERS OF PHOTOGRAPHIC PORTRAITURE

Long before the invention of photography there was a widespread desire for cheap portraiture. For centuries good portraits had remained the luxury of people who could afford the fees of a leading miniature painter or even a portrait in oils by a well-known artist.

Miniature painting

Began early in the sixteenth century, reached its zenith of popularity around 1800, and was eclipsed by photography in the mid-nineteenth century.

32 Miniature of a gentleman c. 1815. 2¼" x 3". In red morocco case. A fine portrait painted in the style of Sir Thomas Lawrence, with a background of red curtains.

Silhouettes

The pioneer of cheap portraiture was the silhouette. Since it was sometimes semi-mechanically produced, demanded a sitting of only a few minutes, and could be easily copied, the silhouette may be regarded as an ancestor of the photographic portrait by which it was superseded. Black profile portraits were well established by the time they were nicknamed silhouette after Etienne de Silhouette, Louis XV's Finance Minister, whose drastic economies caused wits to call "silhouette" anything that was cheap and skimpy. Though the first silhouettes were made in the seventeenth century, they became fashionable only in the second half of the eighteenth century, and began to go out of favor after the introduction of the

14

daguerreotype portrait. Silhouettes were painted on card, glass, ivory, plaster, etc., in which case they were in the nature of a profile miniature portrait filled in with black; or they were cut out of black paper free-hand and pasted on a white, or occasionally colored, background; or the profile could be cut out of white paper and mounted on black.

Apparatus was devised as an aid in making silhouettes. The sitter was posed in a special chair to support the head and whole body. The shadow of the head, cast by the light of a wax candle, was received on an oiled-paper screen behind clear glass, fixed on one side of the posing-chair (see No. 36). The artist stood or sat behind the screen, the frame of which had a movable arm-rest to steady his hand. The life-size outline of the shadow which he traced was then usually reduced to a small size by using a pantograph or "parallelogrammum delineatorum" invented early in the seventeenth century by Christopher Scheiner.

33 Silhouette of a gentleman c. 1785 by John Miers (1758-1821) painted in black on plaster of Paris. 2¾" x 3¼". In Georgian pearwood frame with black and gold enamel surround.

34 Silhouette of a lady c. 1792, painted in bluish-black on white paper. 3" x 3¾". In contemporary black pearwood frame.

35 Silhouette of a young gentleman c. 1835, painted in black with touches of gold on white card. 2" x 3". In red morocco case.

36 Johann Kaspar Lavater

Essai sur la Physiognomonie (sic)
First French edition. La Haye 1781-6.

Lavater, the famous Swiss physiognomist, believed that the silhouette, although the least finished form of portraiture, was the most truthful and revealing of character, and consequently used about 150 silhouettes among the illustrations in his monumental work. Vol. II contains Lavater's chapter on silhouettes and the plate shown illustrates a form of silhouette-making apparatus in common use, invented by Johann Rudolf Schellenberg.

37 Painted silhouette on glass, a lady c. 1790, with colored dress and background. 5" x 7". In contemporary pearwood frame.

This is the kind of picture Wedgwood copied on paper or white leather sensitized with silver chloride (see No. 22). Shown with it is a modern reconstruction of what Wedgwood's attempts must have looked like.

Wedgwood portrait plaques

Another popular form of portraiture—restricted, however, to famous people—were the Wedgwood portrait plaques made of jasper ware. From original portrait reliefs by well-known artists, these pottery plaques were produced for sale in fairly large editions from 1776 onward.

38 John Wesley (1703-1791). Blue Wedgwood portrait plaque c. 1780. 2¾" x 3½". In contempory pearwood frame.

Physionotrace

While the silhouette was at the height of its popularity a novel technique for executing mechanically and rapidly small and cheap portraits was introduced in France—the physionotrace. The machine invented in 1786 by Gilles Louis Chrètien was a wooden framework containing a vertical pantograph, and a reticulated "sight" to keep the operator's eye always in the same position relative to the sitter, who was posed in profile behind the apparatus. When the artist moved the pointer over the outlines of the face, the pencil at the end of the pantograph drew these outlines on paper in nearly natural size. By a second pantograph operation the portrait was reduced to 2" x 2¾" in diameter, and subsequently engraved on a copper plate in the usual way, from which a large number of prints could be pulled. These were usually hand-colored. Physionotrace portraiture was almost exclusively confined to Paris, though it was for short periods practiced in Brussels, Hamburg, New York, Philadelphia, Washington, and Baltimore. It died a natural death before the introduction of photography.

39 Physionotrace of J. B. de Pille, dated 1790. Drawn with the physionotrace by Fouquet, engraved by Chrètien. Hand-colored.

40 Physionotrace of a gentleman c. 1790. Drawn and engraved by Edmé Quenedey. In contemporary wooden frame.

41 Physionotrace of Madame Viannet c. 1793. Drawn by Fouquet, engraved by Chrétien. Hand-colored.

Camera lucida

The last invention preceding photographic portraiture was neither exclusively employed for portraits nor was its use as widespread as the others. The *camera lucida* invented by William Hyde Wollaston in 1807 was an optical instrument aiding the artist, which had a more extensive use for landscapes than for portraiture (see Nos. 28, 29).

42 Lithographed portrait of William Hyde Wollaston, inventor of the *camera lucida,* from a sketch made with the aid of this instrument by Sir Francis Chantrey, c. 1828. 6¼ " x 9".

Photographic miniatures

Photographs over-painted by a miniaturist, were made by Henry Collen, a professional miniature painter and first licensee of Fox Talbot's Calotype patent from 1841 until about 1844. Antoine Claudet, a leading London daguerreotypist, also took out a license from Talbot, in 1844. Claudet's daguerreotype and Calotype portraits were sometimes tinted and painted respectively by his associate L. Mansion, a former miniature painter. The metallic daguerreotypes could only be tinted, but paper photographs could be so heavily over-painted that the photograph itself cannot be discerned, yet a greater reality pervades the portrait than in ordinary miniatures—as was claimed at the time for these photographic miniatures.

A. Claudet and L. Mansion (attributed to)

43 A gentleman c. 1848. 3¼ " x 4½ ". Calotype by Claudet over-painted by Mansion. In contemporary leather case.

A. Claudet and E. T. Parris

44 A lady 1858. 4½ " x 6". On the back is written: "Photographed by A. Claudet, painted by E. T. Parris. 8/58." In contemporary red morocco case bearing Claudet's name and address and the Royal coat-of-arms—Claudet was photographer to Queen Victoria. This is the only known occasion on which Claudet collaborated with Parris, a fashionable portrait painter, regular exhibitor at the Royal Academy, painter of Queen Victoria's Coronation picture and of a famous panorama of London.

MILESTONES IN PHOTOGRAPHY

Note. Up to about 1925 the photographs exhibited are nearly all original contact prints, not enlargements in spite of their sometimes astonishing size. Only occasionally when the original photograph is contained in an album or is too small for exhibition purposes, a reproduction is shown, which is marked "Rep." in the catalogue. In the dimensions stated, width precedes height.

Joseph Nicéphore Niépce, 1765-1833

French landowner and amateur scientist. Inventor of photography and photo-etching, both of which he called "Heliography."

Niépce experimented with photography from 1816 on; ten years later he succeeded in making the first permanent camera photograph (No. 47). In December, 1829, he entered into partnership with L. J. M. Daguerre in order to perfect his invention.

45 Portrait of Nicéphore Niépce. Gouache by C. Laguiche, c. 1800. (rep.)

46 "Notice sur l'Héliographie." Two manuscripts by Niépce concerning his epoch-making invention, dated 8 December, 1827. He submitted these, together with Nos. 47, 48, and other Heliographs to King George IV of England and the Royal Society, London, in the hope of obtaining their patronage for his invention.

47 The world's first photograph, 1826. View from the window of Niépce's work-room at his house Gras near Châlon-sur-Saone, taken on a polished pewter plate 8″ x 6½″, coated with light-sensitive bitumen of Judea. After an exposure of approximately eight hours the plate was washed with a mixture of lavender-oil and white petroleum which dissolved the parts of the bitumen which had not been hardened by light. In original gilt frame. This is the only surviving camera photograph by Niépce, and together with Nos. 46 and 48 was rediscovered by the Gernsheims in February 1952 after several years of searching for them.

47a Label on the back of the world's first photograph (rep.) stating: "Les premiers résultats obtenus spontanément par l'action de la lumière" (the first results obtained spontaneously by the action of light), to which has been added by Francis Bauer, to whom the inventor presented the picture: "Monsieur Niépce's first successful experiment of fixing permanently the image of nature." The date 1827 is when Niépce presented it.

47b The modern reproduction, made with great difficulty by the Kodak Research Laboratories at Harrow near London in 1952, gives a clear picture of the world's first photograph, although the necessity of reproducing it by diagonal lighting has exaggerated the surface irregularities of the pewter plate, making the photograph look somewhat like a reproduction of a *pointilliste* painting by Seurat. Owing to the long exposure (approx. 8 hours) the sun appears to be shining on both sides of the courtyard at the same time.

48 Photo-etching of a copper-plate engraving of Cardinal d'Amboise. (Minister of Louis XII). 5½″ x 8″. One of two prints pulled in February, 1827, by the Parisian engraver Lemaitre from a light-etched pewter plate produced by Niépce the previous year. The photo-etching was produced by laying the engraving of the Cardinal, made transparent by waxing it, on a pewter plate with a light-sensitive coating of bitumen and exposing it to sunshine for two or three hours. The parts of the bitumen unaffected by light were then dissolved away with a

mixture of lavender-oil and white petroleum, as in No. 47. The plate was etched with acid, and no retouching with engraving tools was necessary. The portrait of Cardinal d'Amboise was Niépce's most successful photo-etching. As each heliograph was a direct positive, he hoped to be able to multiply his *camera obscura* pictures also as photo-etchings, but the image was too faint.

L. J. M. Daguerre, 1787-1851

French artist, inventor (with Charles-Marie Bouton) of the Diorama, and of the first practicable photographic process. He entered into partnership with Niépce in December, 1829, but the first successful daguerreotype, an improvement on heliography, dates from May, 1837—four years after the death of Niépce. The important discovery of Daguerre was the possibility of developing the latent image with mercury vapor, thus reducing the exposure time from at least eight hours to 20-30 minutes. After unsuccessful attempts to exploit his process commercially, Daguerre succeeded in interesting the French government in it, and pensions were granted to him and to Niépce's son. Daguerre's patron, the famous astronomer and politician Arago, made the daguerreotype process known to the world at a joint session of the French Academy of Science and Academy of Arts at the Institut de France on 19 August, 1839. Five days earlier, however, Daguerre had patented his invention in England, though everywhere else it was free for all to use.

The daguerreotype was a sensation, as no earlier invention had been, and within a few weeks had conquered Europe and America. In 1839-40 no fewer than 32 editions of Daguerre's manual of the daguerreotype process were published in altogether eight languages, apart from other publications on the subject.

49 Portrait of L. J. M. Daguerre from a daguerreotype by E. Thiésson, 1844. (rep.)

50 Broadsheet on the Diorama. "View of Montmartre," 1830. Daguerre's and Bouton's gigantic paintings (22 x 14 metres, 24 x 15½ yards) attained an astonishing illusion of reality. The picture was painted on both sides of semi-transparent material and illuminated with changing light effects from the front and behind.

Daguerre's dioramas enjoyed enormous success in Paris from 1822 until 1839 and in London from 1823 until 1852 (in the later years with diorama paintings by other artists). Similar dioramas were shown in Breslau, Berlin, Cologne, Stockholm.

51 *MS letter from Daguerre* to Monsieur Degascq, dated 1 July, 1839, regarding the winding-up of the Paris Diorama, which was destroyed by fire on 8 March.

52 *Daguerreotype by Daguerre.* View of Notre Dame and the Ile de la Cité, Paris. 1838-39. 20.5 x 15.5 cm. 8″ x 6″. One of the seventeen surviving daguerreotypes by the inventor himself.

53 *Rapport de M. Arago sur le Daguerréotype.* 34 pages. Arago's official publication of the daguerreotype process at the Institut de France on 19 August, 1839. Appearing the same month, this rare brochure is the first French separate publication on photography.

54 *Historique et description des procédés du daguerréotype et du diorama par Daguerre.* 76 pp., 6 plates and portrait of Daguerre. Paris, Alphonse Giroux et Cie. (September) 1839. Daguerre's manual on his and Niépce's process, published by order of the French Government.

55 *Historique et description des procédés du daguerréotype et du diorama, rédigé par Daguerre.* 88 pp., 6 plates and portrait of Daguerre. Paris, Lerebours et Susse Frères (November) 1839. This is probably the fourth French edition and contains additional practical information by the publishers, and the first instructions for making portraits.

56 *History and Practice of Photogenic Drawing on the True Principles of the Daguerreotype, with the new method of Dioramic Painting: published by order of the French Government.* By the inventor, L. J. M. Daguerre. XII pp. + 76 pp. and 6 plates. London. September, 1839. First English edition of Daguerre's manual.

57 *Daguerres ausführliche Beschreibung seiner grossen Erfindung, oder die Kunst, auf die beste Art die so höchst merkwürdigen Lichtbilder zu verfertigen. Gemein-fässlich von Daguerre selbst mitgetheilt.* 108 pp. and 6 plates. Stuttgart (September) 1839. Possibly the earliest and doubtless the first complete German edition of Daguerre's manual.

58 *Description pratique du procédé nommé le daguerréotype . . . par Daguerre.* 45 pp. and 6 plates. Genoa, 1839. This edition in the French language which appeared in the Kingdom of Sardinia, is the first Italian edition of Daguerre's manual.

59 *El daguerotipo (sic), explicacion del descubrimiento que acaba de hacer, y a que ha dado nombre M. Daguerre.* xxxviii pp. + 52 pp. and 6 plates. Madrid 1839. Probably the first of the three Spanish editions of Daguerre's manual which appeared in 1839.

60 *Exposicion historica y descripcion de los procedimientos del daguerreotipo y del diorama.* Translated from the most recent French edition, corrected and considerably augmented with notes, additions and explanations by D. I. Hysern y Molleras. 119 pp. + xvi pp. and 7 plates. Madrid 1839. Probably the third and certainly the fullest of the three Spanish editions.

61 *Das Geheimnis der Daguerrotypie (sic) oder die Kunst: Lichtbilder durch die camera obscura zu erzeugen. Mit einer Anweisung zur Bereitung des photogenischen Papieres nach Talbot und Daguerre.* 68 pp. Leipzig and Graz, (July) 1839. The author, who signs his foreword "F-n," is probably Karl von Frankenstein, a Graz writer of technical brochures. This extremely rare incunable of photography is the first separate publication in the world concerning Daguerre's invention; nevertheless the greater part of the information about the daguerreotype is imaginary, for Daguerre did not reveal his secret process until three weeks later! The author believed that daguerreotypes were made on paper!

62 *Daguerreotipo. Scoperta Ottico-Pittorica per ottenere le immagini degli oggetti col mezzo della luce. Metodo dei signori Daguerre e Niépce con note sul metodo di Talbot per preparare le carte fotogeniche.* 8 pp. Bologna (4 September) 1839. First separate publication on photography in the Italian language, and the fourth in the world. (see Nos. 53, 61 and 65). The author is unknown.

63 *Relazione intorno al dagherrotipo* (sic). Macedonio Melloni's report to the Academy of Science in Naples, 12 November, 1839. 35 pp. (November) 1839. This publication comes from the library of King Ferdinand II of Naples and Sicily.

William Henry Fox Talbot, 1800-1877

English landowner, scientist and inventor in 1835 of photography on paper, which he called "Photogenic Drawing." In January, 1839 when Talbot heard of Daguerre's invention he published his own in order to establish priority. Later it became evident that the two processes were quite different. Daguerre's was more perfect technically but produced only single pictures and was therefore a *cul-de-sac*. Talbot's negative-positive principle, on the other hand, was of the greatest significance for the future of photography.

In September, 1840, Talbot discovered the possibility of developing the latent image, whereby the exposure in the camera was reduced from about an hour to one or two minutes. He patented this improved process, called Calotype, in February, 1841.

Talbot was also a pioneer in the field of photographically illustrated books, photo-engraving *(Photoglyphic Engraving)* and "spark" photography of rapidly moving objects.

64 Portrait of W. H. Fox Talbot from a daguerreotype by Antoine Claudet, 1844. (rep.)

65 *Some account of the art of Photogenic Drawing, or the process by which natural objects may be made to delineate themselves without the aid of the artist's pencil.* 13 pp. London (February) 1839. This brochure which was privately published by Talbot in a small edition consists of his report to the Royal Society on 31 January, 1839, and constitutes the first separate publication in the world on photography.

66 "Account of some recent improvements in photography." Talbot's report on his invention of the Calotype to the Royal Society on 10 June, 1841, in the *Philosophical Magazine,* Vol. XIX, 1841.

66a *The Calotype Familiarly Explained, being a Treatise on its Objects and Uses, and the Methods of preparing the Sensitive Paper and taking Pictures by the Agency of Light,* by W. Raleigh Baxter. London 1842. 24 pp. The first manual on the Calotype process.

67 *Die Kalotypische Portraitirkunst,* by F. A. W. Netto. 36 pp. + 3 plates. Quedlinburg and Leipzig, 1842. The first foreign manual on Talbot's process, giving instructions on how to take portraits, landscapes etc., in a few minutes. Particularly interesting is that the author recommends the book especially for artists.

The following uncut prints by Talbot are unusually well-preserved proof prints from his own collection. In general, Calotypes (or Talbotypes) were insufficiently rinsed or fixed and are therefore frequently in a very faded condition.

68 Photogenic Drawing of a printed page by Caxton. c. 1840. 7½″ x 9″

69 Photogenic drawing of an engraving. c. 1841. 7¼″ x 9″

70 Photogenic Drawing of lace. c. 1842. 7½″ x 9″

71 The chess players. Calotype. c. 1842. 5¾″ x 7¾″

72 Street scene in Paris. Calotype. 1843. 7″ x 6¾″

73 "The Open Door." Calotype. 1844. 7¾″ x 5¾″

74 The bridge at St. John's College, Cambridge. Calotype. c. 1844. 9¾″ x 7¾″

75 The cloisters at Lacock Abbey, Talbot's house. Calotype. c. 1845. 8¼″ x 6½″

76 View of York Minster. Calotype. July 1845. 8″ x 6½″

77 St. George's Chapel, Windsor. Calotype. 1846. 8″ x 6″

78 *The Pencil of Nature,* qto., London 1844-46. The world's first photographically illustrated book was published in six parts and contains altogether 24 Calotypes. Part I, published on 29 June, 1844, is exhibited.

79 MS letter dated 23 June, 1844, from Talbot to the editor of *The Literary Gazette,* explaining the importance of this new method of book illustration, and the difficulties he experienced in producing it.

80 *Sun Pictures in Scotland,* qto., with 23 Calotypes by Talbot. London 1845. The second photographically illustrated book. In order to avoid any possible misunderstanding, Nos. 78 and 80 contained a printed notice to the reader stating that the illustrations were produced solely by the influence of light.

81 Portal of the church of St. Trophime at Arles, France. Photo-engraving by Talbot. 14 July, 1866. 7¾″ x 5½″

82 The Church of St. Maurice, Vienne, France. Photo-engraving by Talbot. 12 July, 1866. 5½″ x 7¾″

Nos. 81 and 82 are Talbot's own proof prints, produced by his improved process of Photoglyphic Engraving which he patented in 1858. They were made purely photographically without any retouching by the engraver.

Abel Niépce de Saint-Victor, 1805-1870

Officer in the French Army, and inventor of the albumen on glass process—the first practical photographic process on glass (1847), which owing to its slowness was only suitable for architecture, still-life and dia-positives. Niépce de Saint-Victor also greatly improved heliography, the invention of his cousin Nicéphore Niépce, and succeeded in making photo-engravings from camera photographs of nature—the goal that his cousin had set himself.

83 **Portrait of Abel Niépce de Saint-Victor** from a heliogravure by A. Riffaut. 1856. (rep.)

84 "Note sur la photographie sur verre." Niépce de Saint-Victor's report to the Academy of Science, Paris. 12 June, 1848. First publication of the albumen on glass process, in *Comptes rendus,* Vol. XXVI, 1848.

Frederick Scott Archer, 1813-1857

English sculptor and photographer, inventor of the wet collodion process on glass (1850) which in a short time superseded all other photographic processes. The collodion process remained in general use for over thirty years, and is still employed in block-making. A glass plate was coated with collodion containing potassium iodide and then sensitized in a silver-nitrate bath. Exposure, and development with pyrogallic acid or ferrous sulphate, had to take place while the collodion was still moist. The negative was fixed with either sodium thiosulphate or potassium cyanide. Archer's collodion process was more complicated than the daguerreotype or Calotype, and since sensitizing, developing, fixing and rinsing had all to be done on the spot, it was necessary to take along a complete darkroom outfit for out-door photography. All these disadvantages were, however, compensated for by the short exposure, which was reduced to seconds instead of minutes (except for large plate sizes). Later, various dry collodion processes were introduced, which were considerably slower than wet collodion, but more convenient when traveling.

85 **Portrait of Frederick Scott Archer** from an ambrotype by R. Cade. 1855. (rep.)

86 "On the use of collodion in photography," First publication of Archer's epoch-making invention in *The Chemist,* London. March 1851.

Dr. Richard Leach Maddox, 1816-1902

English doctor and microscopist, inventor of the first practicable silver-bromide gelatine emulsion (1871) which after considerable improvement by Burgess, Kennett, and Bennett led to the mass production of dry plates from c. 1878 onward. Photographers no longer had to prepare their own negative material but could buy ready-made plates in shops, as today. Exposure times were only 1/10th to 1/20th as compared with wet collodion, and were no longer measured in seconds, but in fractions of a second. Instantaneous photography opened up vast new fields of application.

87 **Portrait of Dr. R. L. Maddox** from a photograph by W. E. Debenham. c. 1880. (rep.)

Dr. Hermann Wilhelm Vogel, 1834-1898

Founder and director of the photographic laboratory at the Royal Industrial Institute,

Berlin; professor of photochemistry at the Institute of Technology in Berlin from 1879 onward. Discovered in December 1873 the increased sensitivity of negative material to green and yellow rays by the addition of suitable aniline dyes. Up to that time negative material had been sensitive chiefly to the blue rays, and therefore more or less "color blind." Vogel's discovery of color sensitizing laid the foundation for isochromatic and panchromatic negative material which made possible the reproduction of objects and paintings in the correct tone-scale, and eventually three-color photography.

88 Portrait of Dr. H. W. Vogel from a photograph by Loescher & Petsch, c. 1894. (rep.)

89 *Die Photographie farbiger Gegenstände in den richtigen Tonverhältnissen.* First edition of H. W. Vogel's important manual. Berlin 1885.

George Eastman, 1854-1932

The American founder of the Eastman Kodak Company in Rochester furthered photography for the man in the street by two epoch-making novelties—the Kodak rollfilm camera (1888) and celluloid rollfilm (1889). With the Kodak 48 photographs could be taken on a thin transparent celluloid film. In 1914 the U. S. Appeals Court, after a complicated lawsuit lasting twelve years, decided that the original inventor of this film was the Rev. Hannibal Goodwin of Newark, and the Eastman Kodak Co. settled with the owners of Goodwin's patent for five million dollars in cash.

90 Portrait of George Eastman from a photograph by Nahum Luboshez. 1922. (rep.)

91 A celluloid rollfilm negative, 2¼" diameter, taken with a Kodak in 1889 by Queen Alexandra of England (when Princess of Wales).

DAGUERREOTYPES

A silvered copper plate (bought ready-made) was sensitized with iodine vapor and after exposure in the camera the latent image was developed with mercury vapor, fixed with sodium thiosulphate (hyposulphite of soda) and rinsed. The result was a direct positive picture which could not be multiplied, and the delicate surface had to be protected by a cover-glass against oxidation and rubbing.

The most important application of the daguerreotype was to portraiture, which was only possible after considerable improvements to Daguerre's process and apparatus had been made by others. Alexander Wolcott's metal-mirror camera without lens (1840) and Voigtländer's metal camera with the fast Petzval lens (1841) were optical improvements: chemical acceleration processes were devised by J. F. Goddard (1840), Franz Kratochwiela (1841), Antoine Claudet (1841) and others. The world's first public

photographic portrait studio was opened by Alexander Wolcott in New York at the beginning of March, 1840, and on 23 March, 1841, followed Richard Beard's studio in London. In Europe the daguerreotype remained in favor until about 1855; in America until 1860.

Rufus Anson

One of the leading daguerreotypists in New York.

92 A little girl. c. 1850. 2¼" x 2¾".

Platt D. Babbitt

American daguerreotypist who was granted a monopoly in photography on the American side of the Niagara Falls in 1853.

93 View of the Niagara Falls with four ladies and one gentleman. c. 1854. 7¼" x 5¼".

94 Niagara River with a man named John Avery stranded on rocks in the middle. July 1853. 3⅝″ x 2⅞″. An early news photograph.

Richard Beard

Patentee of the daguerreotype process in Britain, and originally a coal merchant in London. Beard in June 1840 bought Wolcott's English patent rights for his mirror camera. After his employee J. F. Goddard had worked out a method of chemical acceleration of the plate, Beard opened the first public daguerreotype portrait studio in Britain — probably in Europe — on 23 March 1841 at the Royal Polytechnic Institution, London. In June of the same year he became sole patentee of the daguerreotype in England, Wales, and the Colonies. In March 1842 he patented a method of coloring daguerreotypes. Business proved immensely successful and further studios were soon opened by Beard in London and the provinces. His quickly earned fortune was lost in several protracted lawsuits in connection with his daguerreotype patent and he was declared bankrupt in June 1850, three years before the patent ran out. Beard then concentrated on making daguerreotypes to be copied as steel-engravings for illustrated books such as John Tallis's *History and Description of the Crystal Palace* 1851 and Henry Mayhew's *London Labour and the London Poor* 1851.

95 Mrs. Fitz. 1841. 1½″ x 2″. One of the earliest surviving daguerreotype portraits.

96 A lady. 1842. 1⅜″ x 2″

97 A gentleman. Delicately hand-tinted. c. 1845. 1¾″ x 2¼″

98 A gentleman with top hat. Hand-colored. c. 1845. 2½″ x 3″

99 A young gentleman. October 1845. 1½″ x 2″. In black miniature frame.

100 A gentleman, seated. Hand-colored, with cloud background. October 1849. 2½″ x 3⅜″

Antoine Claudet, 1797-1867

The leading daguerreotypist in Britain and eminent photographic scientist. Born at Lyon, France, Claudet settled in London in 1827 as an importer of sheet-glass and glass domes. In 1839 he learned the daguerreotype process from the inventor himself and introduced it into Britain, having also purchased the monopoly right to import French daguerreotypes and Daguerre's apparatus. Claudet opened the second photographic studio in Britain, on the roof of the Royal Adelaide Gallery, London, in June 1841, having independently devised a method of chemical acceleration. He patented the red darkroom light and the use of painted backgrounds. In 1853 Claudet was appointed photographer to Queen Victoria.

101 A gentleman. c. 1842. 2″ x 2½″

102 A middle-aged lady. Hand-colored. c. 1850. 2″ x 2½″. (See also Nos. 43, 44)

J. P. Girault de Prangey, 1804-1892

French landowner, historian of architecture, and amateur daguerreotypist; took over a thousand daguerreotypes on a journey in the Middle East 1841-1843, all being dated. His daguerreotypes are unusually large for the first years of the process, and being landscapes and architectural views are extremely rare—in Europe at any rate. In the United States the daguerreotype was more extensively used for landscapes than elsewhere. In the case of tall architectural subjects Girault de Prangey took two on one plate and cut it in half (Nos. 103-107).

103 Portal of Genoa Cathedral, with statue. 1842. 3¾″ x 9½″

104 View of Rome. 1842. 9½″ x 3¾″

105 Church of S. Luigi, Rome. 1842. 3¾″ x 9½″

106 Minaret of the Mosque of Kalaun, Cairo. 1843. 3¾″ x 9½″

107 Temple of Jupiter at Baalbek. 1843. 3¾″ x 9½″

108 Church of S. Theodore, Athens. 1842. 9½″ x 7½″

109 The Cathedral, Athens (detail). 1842. 9½″ x 7½″

110 Etruscan tombs at Castel d'Asso. 1842. 9½″ x 7½″

Cornelius Jabez Hughes, 1819-1884

Started as assistant to J. E. Mayall in London, 1847, two years later bought the business of a Glasgow daguerreotypist, and in 1855 took over Mayall's first London studio, and made collodion portraits. From 1862 onward, Jabez Hughes had a portrait studio at Ryde, Isle of Wight, where he was appointed photographer to Queen Victoria at Osborne, I. of W. Published two popular manuals on the collodion process.

111 A lady, seated. c. 1853-54. 3¼″ x 4½″

Charles Jacquard, Sedan

112 Eugène Hulin. 3 October 1849. 2¾″ x 3¼″

William Edward Kilburn

Prominent London portrait photographer from 1846 until about 1865. Appointed photographer to Queen Victoria, 1847.

113 An officer. Hand-colored. 1853. 2½″ x 3½″

114 A lady. Hand-colored, with cloud background. c. 1851. 2¾″ x 3½″

John Edwin Mayall, 1810-1901

A daguerreotypist in Philadelphia 1842-46, Mayall opened a portrait studio in London early in 1847, originally practicing as "Professor Highschool" and calling his studio "The American Daguerreotype Institution." Mayall was the first to make composition pictures, and exhibited a "Bacchus and Ariadne" measuring 24″ x 15″ at the Great Exhibition, 1851. This was acclaimed as a great technical feat, and is believed to be the largest daguerreotype ever made. In 1855 Mayall moved to Regent Street, and during the *carte-de-visite* period became the most prosperous photographer in Britain. (For Mayall's later career see page 48.)

115 A gentleman. Hand-colored. c. 1850. 2¼″ x 2¾″

116 A gentleman. Hand-colored. c. 1850. 2¾″ x 3¾″

117 Two ladies. c. 1849. 2½″ x 3″

118 A middle-aged lady. Hand-colored. c. 1850. 4¼″ x 6″

Victor Plumier, Paris

119 A young gentleman. c. 1850. 2½″ x 3¾″

Carl Ferdinand Stelzner, c. 1806-1894

Born at Flensburg, Stelzner was originally a well-known German miniature painter before he opened a daguerreotype studio in Hamburg in 1842. In the mid-fifties his sight failed and the studio was run by an employee. Together with Hermann Biow, another Hamburg daguerreotypist, Stelzner ranks as one of Germany's best daguerreotypists.

120 Fräulein Reimer, Frau Stelzner, Fräulein Mathilde von Braunschweig. c. 1842. 2½″ x 2¾″

William Telfer

London daguerreotypist from c. 1848, whose "Royal Photographic Establishment" was in Regent Street.

121 A young lady in mauve bonnet. Hand-colored. c. 1849. 1½″ x 2¼″

122 An elderly lady. Hand-colored. c. 1848. 1½″ x 2¼″

Unknown daguerreotypists

123 An old lady, with view of Danzig. German. c. 1845. 2½″ x 3″

124 Colonel William Blake. Hand colored, with cloud background. c. 1848. 2¼″ x 2½″

125 Two portraits in one case: a young lady and a young gentleman. c. 1845. Each 2¼″ x 2¾″

126 An old gentleman. 1850. 3½″ x 4½″. In decorative gold frame.

127 Sir Henry Bessemer. c. 1848. 3″ x 3½″

128 An old gentleman. c. 1845. 3¼″ x 4⅜″

129 A lady and two gentlemen. c. 1846. 5½" x 4½"

130 A gentleman with painted sky. c. 1845. 2⅜" x 3¾"

131 A lady. Slightly tinted. c. 1845. Austrian. 2½" x 3"

132 Family group. c. 1845. Austrian. 2¾" x 3¾"

133 Young lady in striped dress. c. 1845. French or Italian. 3¾" x 2½"

134 A lady and gentleman, seated. c. 1848. American. 2¼" x 2¾"

135 Gioachino Rossini. c. 1850. 2½" x 3"

136 Family group of eight people. Tinted. c. 1852-3. 8" x 6½"

137 Three men named Billings, seated. c. 1845. American. 3½" x 2¾"

138 A gentleman. c. 1845. American. 2¼" x 2⅜"

139 A gentleman. c. 1845. 1¾" x 2¼"

STEREOSCOPIC DAGUERREOTYPES

The reflecting stereoscope, invented by Sir Charles Wheatstone in 1832 in order to demonstrate binocular vision, was used to observe simple geometrical designs as apparently solid bodies. In 1841 photographs on paper were used instead of drawings. In order to attain a similar effect with shiny daguerreotypes the Scottish scientist Sir David Brewster designed the refracting stereoscope (1849) — a type which had already been invented by Wheatstone. Brewster's stereoscope aroused much interest at the Great Exhibition in London two years later. Claudet, Mayall, Kilburn, and a few other leading London daguerreotypists took the necessary double pictures with two cameras side by side. The twin-lens stereo camera proposed by Brewster (1849) was not constructed until 1853, and put on the market in 1856. With it began the craze for stereoscopy.

All stereoscopic photographs consist of two separate pictures 2⅜" x 2¾" on a standard mount 6¾" x 3¼".

Antoine Claudet

140 "The Geography Lesson." 1851. One of the earliest stereoscopic daguerreotypes.
141 Bishop Spencer of Jamaica and his daughter Mrs. Harvey. 1857. Hand colored. Contained in Claudet's folding pocket stereoscope which he patented in March 1853.

W. E. Kilburn

142 A lady and gentleman. 1852-53. Contained in a folding pocket stereoscope of a slightly different type from Claudet's, which Kilburn patented in January 1853.

Unknown English daguerreotypist

142a Still-life with guitare, sculpture and Brewster stereoscope c. 1851.

Unknown French daguerreotypist

143 An odalisque. Hand-colored. c. 1852.

144 An artist's model. Hand-colored. c. 1852.

Caricatures

145 "La Daguerréotypomanie." Lithograph 14" x 10¾", by Théodore Maurisset, Paris. December 1839. The first caricature of photography.

146 "La Patience est la vertue des ânes." Lithograph 7½" x 9¼", by Honoré Daumier in *Le Charivari,* Paris, July 1840.

147 "Position réputée la plus comode pour avoir un joli portrait au Daguerréotype." Lithograph 9¾" x 8¾", by Honoré Daumier in *Les Bons Bourgeois,* Paris 1844.

148 "Le portrait au Daguerréotype." Lithograph 7" x 8½", by an unknown artist signing "CH3" in *Le Charivari,* Paris, July 1845.

With the Calotype process a paper negative was produced, from which any number of positive copies could be made. The process was much simpler than the daguerreotype. Good-quality writing paper was made light-sensitive by brushing on a solution of silver nitrate and potassium iodide. After exposure the latent image was developed by applying a mixture of gallic acid and silver nitrate, fixed with sodium thiosulphate and rinsed. To make the grain of the paper invisible and speed up printing, Calotype negatives were frequently waxed before printing.

In Gustave Le Gray's waxed paper process (1851), a variant of the Calotype, thin paper was waxed before taking the picture, resulting in as finely detailed negatives as with the collodion process (see Nos. 153, 154, 197-202).

The best calotypists were in Scotland, where Talbot's process was not patented. In England and on the Continent the Calotype was little used until L. D. Blanquart-Evrard modified the process and reduced the exposure time (1847). However, French Calotypes do not have the rich purple-brown color of the Scottish ones. A short flowering of the Calotype in England began when Talbot relaxed his patent rights for amateurs in August 1852, but already by the mid-fifties the process was largely superseded by wet collodion.

Edouard Baldus, 1820-

French architectural photographer of German origin. Recorded historic monuments in Burgundy, the Dauphiné and Fontainebleau for the French Government Commission for Historic Monuments, 1851. Founder member of the Société Héliographique. Changed from the Calotype to the collodion process in 1854 and made for the government a complete documentation of the new wing of the Louvre in over 1500 detail photographs. Also noted for views, especially of mountains. Invented a photo-engraving process, 1854.

149 Pont du Gard. c. 1850. 17″ x 11″

150 Fortified wall of Avignon. c. 1850. 17½″ x 12½″

151 Maison Carrée. Nîmes. c. 1850. 17½″ x 13¼″
(See also Nos. 302-4)

Maxime Du Camp, 1822-1894

French author and photographer. Learned calotyping from Gustave Le Gray (q.v.) Accompanied by Gustave Flaubert, Du Camp made an archaeological tour of the Middle East for the Ministry of Education, 1849-1851. On this journey he used Blanquart-Evrard's modification of Talbot's process, and the copies for his publication were made at Blanquart-Evrard's printing establishment at Lille.

152 *Egypte, Nubie, Palestine et Syrie.* Paris and London, 1852. A selection of the 30 most interesting photographs, 6⅛″ x 8¼″ from the total of 125 which were published.

Philip Henry Delamotte, 1820-1889

English artist and professor of drawing at London University, began to calotype in the late 'forties and changed over to the collodion process in 1853. Delamotte published a manual of photography and illustrated a number of books with his photographs and drawings. In 1857 Delamotte arranged the photographic department at the Manchester Art Treasures Exhibition of ancient and modern paintings, sculpture and engravings — the first exhibition at which photography was shown alongside the other arts.

153 A landscape. Waxed paper negative. c. 1851. 16⅛″ x 12″

154 Interior of the Crystal Palace, London, after the close of the first international exhibition. Waxed paper negative. March 1852. 16⅛″ x 12″
(See also Nos. 425-430)

Franz Hanfstaengl, 1804-1877

Founder of the lithographic art publishing firm in Munich 1834, the most notable production of which is a set of 190 lithographs of paintings in the Dresden Art Gallery. In 1853 Hanfstaengl changed over to photographic reproductions, and at the same time started a portrait studio where he photographed chiefly celebrities. Became a Councilor to the Royal Court of Bavaria, and in 1868 handed over the running of the art publishing firm — which still exists — to his son Edgar. His relatives Erwin and Teich Hanfstaengl were court photographers in Paris and Dresden respectively during the 1860s.

155   Frau Josephe Schwanthaler, widow of the sculptor Franz Xaver Schwanthaler. 1855. 6¾" x 8¾"

David Octavius Hill, 1802-1870, and Robert Adamson, 1821-1848

The Scottish landscape painter D. O. Hill turned to photography in order to make portrait studies for an enormous painting to immortalize the resignation of over 470 Scottish ministers from the State church in May 1843. He went into partnership with Robert Adamson, who had opened a photographic portrait studio in Edinburgh a few months earlier. After the retirement of Adamson owing to ill health towards the end of 1847, Hill returned to painting. In order to arrive at a short exposure, sunshine was absolutely necessary, so curtains and furniture were brought outside the house and the sitters posed in the open. Hill exhibited the photographs alongside his paintings at the Royal Academy in Edinburgh, and their fame soon spread beyond the borders of Scotland. Today the Calotypes of Hill and Adamson are accounted among the finest achievements of photography.

156   Album entitled *100 Calotype Sketches by D. O. Hill, R.S.A., and R. Adamson. Edinburgh 1845.* 24" x 27"

This is the best preserved of the four surviving albums which Hill and Adamson prepared for sale. It has a title-page painted by Hill, with his photograph in the middle, and contains the best photographs of the two-and-a-half years of Hill's and Adamson's collaboration: portraits, architecture, landscapes, and fisherfolk. The album belonged to the English marine painter Clarkson Stanfield, who preferred the Hill/Adamson photographs even to Rembrandt etchings. Nos. 157-162 are enlarged reproductions from the album.

157   Sailors at Newhaven near Edinburgh. c. 1845. (rep.) Original size 8½" x 6½"

158   Miss Chalmers and her brother. c. 1843. (rep.) Original size 6½" x 8½"

159   The sculptor John Stevens with bust of the Emperor Lucius Verus. 1843-45. (rep.) Original size 6½" x 8½"

160   Rev. George Gilfillan and Dr. Samuel Brown. 1844. (rep.) Original size 8" x 6"

161   Leith harbor. c. 1845. (rep.) Original size 5¾" x 7¾"

162   Cottage at Newhaven. c. 1845. (rep.) Original size 8" x 5¾"

163   Portrait of D. O. Hill by R. Adamson. 1843. 6¼" x 8¼"

164   The Dutch physician Dr. Abraham Capadose. 1843. 5¾" x 8"

165   The Rev. Dr. Thomas Chalmers, founder of the Free Church of Scotland, and his wife. 1843. 11¾" x 9"

166   Six ministers of the Free Church of Scotland. May 1846. 12" x 9¼"

167   James Nasmyth, inventor of the steam hammer. 1843-45. 6" x 7¾"

168   Dr. George Bell. 1843-47. 6" x 7"

169   Gordon Highlanders at Edinburgh Castle. 1843-45. 5¾" x 7¾"

170   The Grierson sisters. 1843-47. 5¾" x 8"

171   George Moir and James Gibson. 1844. 5¾" x 7¾"

172   Sheriff Mark Napier. 1843-47. 5¾" x 7¼"

173   The Marquis of Northampton, President of the Royal Society, London. 1843-47. 5¾" x 8"

174   Sheriff Thomas Gordon and his wife. c. 1845. 11" x 8⅞"

175   The sculptor A. E. Forrester. c. 1845. 9¼" x 11½"

176   Fisherboys at Newhaven near Edinburgh. c. 1845. 7¾" x 5¾"

177 Fishwives at Newhaven. c. 1845. 7¾″ x 5¾″

178 Mrs. Anne Rigby. c. 1844. 6″ x 8″

179 Miss Elizabeth Rigby (later Lady Eastlake). c. 1844. 6″ x 8″

180 Sir Francis Grant, President of the Royal Academy of Arts, London. 1843-47. 5½″ x 8″

181 William Etty, Scottish painter. c. 1843-45. 6″ x 8″

182 The Rev. James Fairbairn reading the Bible to fishwives at Newhaven. c. 1845. 7¾″ x 5¾″

(Nos. 178-182 are carbon prints from Hill's negatives made by T. and R. Annan, Glasgow, 1879-1881).

Dr. Thomas Keith, 1827-1895

Scottish gynaecologist and surgeon; and friend of D. O. Hill. Using the waxed paper process, Dr. Keith took splendid architectural and landscape photographs in and around Edinburgh between 1853-1856, which are in no way inferior to the work of Hill and Adamson, yet remained unknown until a few years ago.

183 Edinburgh Castle. c. 1855. 10¾″ x 9″

184 Tower of Magdalen Chapel, Edinburgh. c. 1855. 9½″ x 10¾″

185 Old houses in Edinburgh. c. 1855. 10″ x 9½″

186 Whitefriars Wynd, an old street in Edinburgh. c. 1855. 9½″ x 10¾″

187 Holyrood Chapel, Edinburgh. c. 1855. 10½″ x 8½″

188 Greyfriars Churchyard, Edinburgh. c. 1855. 10¼″ x 8″

189 Greyfriars Churchyard and Edinburgh Castle. c. 1855. 10¾″ x 9″

190 Old tombs in Greyfriars Churchyard. c. 1855. 10¾″ x 9½″

191 Mackenzie Monument, Edinburgh. c. 1855. Modern contact copy from the original negative. 10″ x 11″

192 Willow trees. c. 1854. Enl. rep. from a waxed paper negative. 8 x 8½″
Attributed to Dr. Thomas Keith

Alois Löcherer, 1815-1862

Professional photographer in Munich from 1847 onward. Well known for portraits of celebrities and for his photo-reportage of the transport of the gigantic statue "Bavaria" from the casting works to its position in front of the Hall of Fame in Munich, 1850.

193 Transport of the torso of "Bavaria". On the cart sit the caster Ferdinand von Miller and the sculptor of the statue, L. von Schwanthaler. 1850. (rep.) 10″ x 12″

194 Chess players. c. 1850. (rep.) Original size 10″ x 12″. Second from left is Franz Xaver Schwanthaler.

Charles Nègre, 1820-1879

French painter and photographer. Began to calotype c. 1850, opened a portrait studio in Paris, but is chiefly known for architectural and *genre* photographs. Founder member of the Société Française de Photographie. Improved various photomechanical processes by which he obtained excellent half-tone pictures: heliogravure (1854), collotype (1856) and photo-galvanography (1861).

195 Notre-Dame, Paris. c. 1850. 8¾″ x 12½″

196 Mediaeval sculpture on the Abbey of St. Gilles du Gard, near Arles. c. 1852. Modern contact copy from original negative. 9½″ x 13″

John Shaw Smith, 1811-1873

Irish landowner. Traveled through Europe and the Near and Middle East 1850-52 and took about 300 paper photographs with the Calotype and waxed-paper processes. Smith was a finer artist than Maxime Du Camp (see No. 152). Whereas, however, Du Camp's photographs immediately became known through his book, Shaw Smith remained unknown until we exhibited his work for the first time in 1951.

197 Turkish cemetery at Pera, Constantinople. November 1851. Waxed paper negative. 10″ x 8″

198 House in Cairo. November 1851. Waxed paper negative. 8″ x 10″

199 Relief on a temple at Thebes. 1851. Waxed paper negative. 10″ x 8″

200 The Great Hall at Karnak. January 1852. Waxed paper negative. 10″ x 8″

201 Capital and architrave of the Temple of Jupiter at Baalbek. May 1852. Waxed paper negative. 10″ x 8″

202 Notre-Dame, Paris, from the south. 1850. Calotype negative and positive. 10″ x 8″

W. H. Fox Talbot, 1800-1877

For Calotypes and Photogenic Drawings by the inventor, see Nos. 68-77.

Unknown photographers

203 Pyramid of Caius Cestius, Rome. November 1858. Calotype negative. 11½″ x 10″

204 Birds' feathers. Cyanotype. c. 1845. 8¼″ x 10¼″

The Cyanotype or blueprint was invented by Sir John Herschel and described by him at a meeting of the Royal Society in February, 1842. On account of its cheapness and permanence the blueprint remained until a few years ago the most widely used method of copying architects' plans and industrial drawings.

AMBROTYPES

The Ambrotype was a variant of the wet collodion process devised by its inventor Frederick Scott Archer in collaboration with Peter W. Fry, and published in July, 1851. An under-exposed collodion negative laid on a black background (or with black varnish coated on the back of the glass) appears as a positive picture. At first it was called "collodion positive on glass." The name "Ambrotype" was introduced in America, as were also the attractive "Union" cases (Nos. 234-249) made of plastic material. Ambrotypes began to go out of fashion in the 1860's after the introduction of the popular **carte-de-visite.**

205 Ambrotype of a gentleman, with half of the black background removed to demonstrate the positive/negative effect. c. 1855. 3½″ x 4¾″

Farmer, Brighton

206 A widow and daughter. Hand colored. c. 1857. 2¾″ x 3¾″

C. Jabez Hughes, London

(For biography see page 23)

207 A lady. Tinted. c. 1858. 2⅝″ x 3½″

David Johnson, Blackburn

208 A gentleman with top hat. c. 1853. 2⅝″ x 3½″

Mansfield & Yeats, Dublin

209 A gentleman. c. 1860. 2⅝″ x 3¾″

George Raft, Brighton

210 A lady. c 1857 2⅝″ x 3″

Unknown photographers

211 Two portraits in a double case: a lady and a gentleman. Tinted. c. 1857. Each 2⅝″ x 3″

212 Two young ladies. c. 1852. 2⅜″ x 3″

213 A family. c. 1860. Two ambrotypes in one case: on one side the mother with two children, on the other side the father. Each 2¼″ x 2¾″

214 Mrs. William Blake. Hand-colored. c. 1856. 2⅝″ x 3½″

215 An officer. Tinted. c. 1856. 1⅝″ x 2″

216 A gentleman. Hand-colored, cloud background. c. 1855. 2¼″ x 2¾″

217 A lady. Hand-colored. c. 1855. 2¼″ x 2¾″

218 A lady. Hand-colored. c. 1857. 2⅝″ x 3½″

219 Lady and gentleman in a carriage at Niagara Falls. c. 1860 7½″ x 6″

220 A young lady. Hand-colored. c. 1857. 1⅝″ x 2″

221 A lady. Blue background. c. 1859. 2¼″ x 2¾″. Case in book form.

222 A lady. Tinted. c. 1860. 1⅝″ x 2″. Case in book form.

223 A gentleman. Hand-colored. c. 1860. 2¼″ x 2¾″

224 Old gentleman with statue. c. 1857. 4″ x 5″

225 An elderly lady. c. 1854. 3⅛″ x 4⅛″

226 Charlotte M. Scott. c. 1855. 1″ x 1⅝″

227 Gentleman with top hat and white dog. c. 1857. 3⅜″ x 4⅜″

228 A young lady. Hand-colored, with landscape background and column. c. 1860. 3⅛″ x 4⅛″

229 A widow with two boys in Scottish costume. Hand-colored. c. 1858. 3½″ x 5″

230 Two ladies and a gentleman. c. 1856. 3⅛″ x 4⅛″

231 A lady in striped dress. Hand-colored. c. 1858. 2¼″ x 2¾″

232 Unusual variant of Ambrotype on leather. A young gentleman. c. 1857. 2½″ x 3″. In lacquer case decorated with mother-of-pearl. A photograph taken direct on sensitized leather was called Pannotype.

"Relievo" Ambrotype

An unusual variant of the Ambrotype, introduced by Thomas C. Lawrence of Greenwich near London. The collodion of the background was carefully scratched off, the back of the portrait coated with black varnish, and the picture mounted on a white background with a thick piece of glass between, giving a strong relief effect.

233 Mother and daughter. Two hand-colored "Relievo" Ambrotypes in one case. c. 1857. 2¼″ x 2¾″

234-249 Selection of 16 American plastic "Union" cases for Ambrotypes and daguerreotypes, with various decorative designs including "Day" and "Night" after Thorwaldsen and scenes from the War of Independence and a portrait of George Washington.

PHOTOGRAPHIC JEWELRY, MEDALS, PAINTINGS, ETC.

250 Gold brooch 1¾″ x 2⅛″ set with daguerreotype of a gentleman, slightly tinted. c.1845. 1⅜″ x 1⅝″. The back of the brooch is sealed with mother-of-pearl.

251 Pinchbeck brooch set with daguerreotype of a gentleman. c. 1843. 1¼″ x 1⅝″

252 Gold brooch 1¾″ x 2″ set with colored photograph of a lady c. 1855. The back of the oval frame with her portrait contains a lock of hair.

253 Gold locket with spring lid, 1¼″ diameter, containing tinted Ambrotype of an old lady. c. 1855. Size of photograph ⅞″.

254 Gold locket 1⅛″ diameter containing photograph of a lady. c. 1860. Initials C.M. engraved on the lid of the locket.

255 Gold locket 1⅛″ diameter containing photograph of a gentleman. c. 1862. Hinged glass frame and lid with initials K.M.R.

256 Mourning pendant for the Prince Consort. Gold pendant with drop pearl, 1⅞″ long, surmounted by the Crown, and containing a photograph of Prince Albert ½″ x 9/16″ oval, in blue enamel frame. On the back is engraved: "To the Marchioness of Ely, in remembrance of the best and greatest of Princes, from his broken-hearted widow, Victoria R., Dec., 1861." (Prince Albert died on 14 December). An identical pendant was presented to Lady Salisbury and is on view in the Long Gallery at Hatfield House.

257 Silver-gilt watch 1¾″ diameter made by Courvoisier Frères on the occasion of

Queen Victoria's becoming Empress of India, 1877. Bears on one cover an enamel photograph of the Queen 1⅛″ x 1¼″ and on the other the same size portrait of an unidentified Indian ruler. Around each portrait is an ornamental border of oriental design inlaid with black, green, red, and blue enamel.

258 Gold tie-pin containing a photograph of John Brown, Queen Victoria's personal attendant, in gold border with the inscription in black enamel: "John, 27 March, 1883." The reverse contains a lock of her hair and is engraved "From V.R.I." In original black morocco case of Collingwood & Co., Jewelers to the Royal Family. The Queen was greatly attached to her attendant, about whom she wanted to write a biography. The present was made two days before his death.

259 Gold pendant in the form of a daisy, ¾″ diameter, with enamelled petals. c. 1865. In the center of the daisy is a magnifying lens 5/16″ diameter, which enlarges a photograph of a lady when in the closed position. By touching a spring, the daisy opens and the magnifying lens enlarges a photograph of a gentleman. The pendant is contained in a heart-shaped green morocco case.

260 Pewter plaque with portrait of Nicéphore Niépce in relief. 5″ diameter. Designed by J. B. Beauvais (signed) after the painting by Berger. Date and purpose unknown.

261 Bronze medal commemorating 50th anniversary of the publication of photography, bearing portraits of Nièpce and Daguerre and the dates 1839-1889. 2⅝″ diameter. Designed by E. Soldi.

262 Bronze medal with portrait of Daguerre designed by Jauner, struck for the Vienna Amateur Photographers' Society as a prize medal in 1888. 2⅜″ diameter.

263 Bronze medal commemorating photography represented as an allegorical female figure with a camera on stand and chemicals, designed by Oudine, 1866. 2¾″ diameter. Bears inscription "Homine dirigente Sol artifex 1838." The *verso* bears a portrait of the Emperor Napoleon III.

264 Bronze medal of the Photographic Society of London, showing Apollo in sun chariot and the date of the Society's foundation, 1853. On the *verso* a portrait of Prince Albert as patron. 2⅜″ diameter. Presented to Henry Stevens in 1882.
(See also No. 1007)

265 Green morocco leather fan 10½″ x 7½″ embossed with gilt decorations, with ivory handle. Made by W. & J. Milne of Edinburgh. Inset are three *cartes* of a family, by W. E. Kilburn, c. 1862.

266 Photograph burnt-in on porcelain: a young lady c. 1887, 7″ x 9″ oval.

267 White and gold Regency-style porcelain vase 7¼″ high with burnt-in photograph of a man, c. 1870.

268 Oil painting 25″ x 30″ of an unknown photographer with wooden box-type camera. His right hand holds the lens cap, the left hand his watch to count the seconds. It may have been painted after a photographic self-portrait. Signed by the artist "W. Widgery 1857."

PHOTOGRAPHS BY THE COLLODION AND GELATINE PROCESSES

It is impossible to judge whether a photograph has been taken on albumen, collodion, gelatine dry plates or film by looking at the print. In any case, such information is valueless from the point of view of the quality of the picture. Unless otherwise stated, the positive paper on which the photograph was copied is toned albumen paper up to about 1900, and thereafter silver bromide paper. From about 1925 onward the pictures exhibited are almost entirely enlargements from small negatives, the size of which is rarely known.

Ansel Adams, b. 1902

American professional photographer since 1930, living in San Francisco. Friend of Edward Weston and founder member of the

F.64 Group (1932). Famous for his nature photographs and also active in other fields of photography. Adams has published a number of books illustrated with his photographs, including *My Camera in the Yosemite Valley* and *My Camera in the National Parks*.

269 Boards and thistles. 1932. 9½" x 7½"

270 Joshua tree, National Monument, California. 7½" x 9½"

271 Rose and driftwood. 1933. 9½" x 7½"

272 Pinecone and eucalyptus leaves. 1933. 9½" x 7½"

273 Grass in the rain. Alaska. 1933. 9½" x 7½"

(All pictures are contact copies).

Antoine Samuel Adam-Salomon, 1811-1881

A successful Parisian sculptor, Adam-Salomon from 1856 onward was also a part-time photographer. His portraits in the style of Old Masters were considered by his contemporaries more artistic than those of Nadar and Carjat; today, however, they seem artificial in pose.

274 Alphonse Karr, author. c. 1865. Carbon print. 7½" x 9½"

275 Charles Garnier, architect. c. 1865. Carbon print. 7¼" x 9¼"

276 Ambroise Thomas, composer. c. 1868. Carbon print. 7½" x 9½"

Josef Albert, 1825-1886

Bavarian court photographer. Perfected the first practicable collotype process in 1868, which was also called "Albertype" and "Heliotype."

277 The Congress of Frankfurt, August, 1863. 9" x 7⅛". In the center is the Emperor Franz Joseph of Austria who convened the congress; on his right King Maximilian II of Bavaria, on his left King George of Hanover. All the German ruling princes appear in the group with the exception of King William I of Prussia whose attendance was prevented by Bismarck.

278 Inauguration of the equestrian monument of King Ludwig I of Bavaria, in the Odeonsplatz, Munich, 25 August, 1862. 8¼" x 6¾"

James Anderson, 1813-1877

The English watercolor painter Isaac Atkinson settled in Rome in 1838 under the name of James Anderson. In 1849 he began photographing antique sculpture and views of Rome, for which there was a great demand by tourists. Later he also made reproductions of paintings. Until a few years ago the world-famous firm of Anderson still flourished under the direction of his grandsons.

279 Base of the Trajan Column, Rome. c. 1858. 11¼" x 14¼"

Victor Angerer, 1839-1894

Austrian portrait photographer in Bad Ischl from 1859 on; joined the portrait studio of his brother Ludwig Angerer, Court photographer in Vienna, in 1873, and continued this business after the latter's death in 1879.

280 The Prater, Vienna. c. 1887. Collotype. 5¾" x 4". Enl. rep.

J. Craig Annan, 1864-1946

Scottish professional photographer, and like his father Thomas Annan, internationally known as a portrait and landscape photographer. Craig Annan introduced into Great Britain Karl Klic's photogravure process. Like Stieglitz and his circle, he made hand-photogravures of his photographs on Japan paper. By his reproductions of the Hill/Adamson Calotypes Annan aroused interest and admiration for these portraits, which for the first time achieved world fame in 1898.

281 Miss Janet Burnet. Photogravure. 1893. 6¾" x 8¼"

282 The artist William Strang. Photogravure. c. 1900. 6¾" x 8¼"

283 Ox-drawn plough. Photogravure. c. 1900. 6¾" x 4¼"

Thomas Annan, 1829-1887

Originally a copperplate engraver, in 1855 Annan opened a photographic studio in

Glasgow and soon became the leading portrait photographer in Scotland. He was a friend of D. O. Hill and Sir Joseph Swan whose carbon process he introduced into Scotland in 1866.

284 Dr. David Livingstone, African explorer and missionary. 1864. Modern contact copy from the original negative. 12″ x 15″

285 Allen Thompson, Harry Rainy and T. T. Jackson: Professors at the University of Glasgow. c. 1866. Carbon prints, each 6½″ x 8½″

286 An old lane in Glasgow. 1868. 9″ x 11¼″

287 An old lane in Glasgow. 1868 8⅞″ x 11″

Nos. 286 and 287 are two pictures from an outstanding photographic documentation of Glasgow slums made between 1868 and 1877 for the City Council. They had the same purpose as the documentation of Jacob Riis (see Nos. 695-699) in New York fifteen to twenty years later.

Edward Anthony, 1818-1888

While training as a civil engineer Anthony learned daguerreotyping from Samuel Morse, and in 1841 photographed the northeastern frontier with Canada, which was in dispute with England—doubtless the earliest use of photography in a government survey. In partnership with J. M. Edwards started a portrait studio in Washington (1842) and photographed all the members of Congress (1843) forming a National Daguerrean Gallery, which was exhibited in New York City, and destroyed by fire, 1852. In 1847 Anthony sold his share in the portrait business and became a dealer in daguerreotype materials. In 1852, founded with his elder brother Henry a firm which later as E. & H. T. Anthony became the principal photographic supply house in the United States. Published stereoscopic views, including the first instantaneous street views of New York (1859).

288 Broadway on a rainy day. August, 1859. Enl. rep. of a stereoscopic photograph, possibly taken for Anthony by William England. (see No. 458)

C. D. Arnold

Professional photographer in Chicago.

289-291 Three views of the Columbian World Exhibition in Chicago, 1893. Platinotypes. From an album of 25 photographs, 20″ x 16½″, presented by the exhibition committee to Viscount Curzon.

Eugéne Atget, 1856-1927

Formerly a French provincial actor, Atget made his now famous documentation of Paris between 1898 and 1927. At the time few people apart from Utrillo were interested in his photographs and Atget died in extreme poverty, leaving about 10,000 pictures of Parisian subjects. It was only in 1930 with the publication of a selection of these photographs in Paris, Leipzig and New York that Atget's work became known to a larger public.

292 Moulin Rouge, Paris. c. 1900. 7″ x 9″

293 Basket shop in Paris. c. 1905. 7″ x 8¾

294 Tree roots at St. Cloud. c. 1910. 7″ x 8¾″

295 Vase at Versailles. c. 1910. 7″ x 8¾″

296 Decorative balustrade in the Grand Trianon. c. 1910. 7″ x 8¾″

297 The Bassin du Nord at Versailles. c. 1910. 7″ x 8¾″

298 Arcade at Versailles. c. 1910. 8¾″ x 7″

Erich Auerbach, b. 1911

Born near Karlsbad (Bohemia) Auerbach joined the *Prager Tagblatt* as music and film critic; then in the early 1930's began photographing for this paper, and in this work found his real vocation. In 1939 Auerbach settled in London, where he worked throughout the war as photographer to the Czechoslovak Government in exile. From 1945 until its demise twelve years later he was staff photographer to *Illustrated,* and now works free-lance, with emphasis on musicians and concert performances. Awarded *Encyclopedia Britannica* prize for feature photography, 1951.

299 Retired civil servant. 1948. 11¾″ x 15½″

300 Art students in Chelsea. 1949. 14½″ x 9¾″

Auguste

French photographer.

301 View of Laval, France. 1861. 12⅝″ x 9¼″

Edouard Baldus, 1820-?

French architectural photographer (see Nos. 149-151. For biography, see page 25).

302 Pont du Gard. c. 1855. 9½″ x 7¼″

303 Church of St. Trophime, Arles. c. 1858. 13¼″ x 18¾″

304 Avignon. c. 1860. 11¼″ x 8¼″

Luigi Bardi

Well-known architectural photographer in Florence.

305 The Baptistery, Pisa. c. 1858. 13½″ x 10¼″

306 Cathedral and Leaning Tower, Pisa. c. 1858. 13½″ x 10¼″

307 The Leaning Tower, Pisa. c. 1858. 10¼″ x 13½″

308 Bronze door of the Baptistery, Florence. c. 1858. 9⅜″ x 13¼″

H. Walter Barnett, 1862-1934

Australian portrait photographer, active in London from 1898 onward photographing society people and celebrities.

309 Mark Twain. 1902. 9½″ x 12¼″

310 Auguste Rodin. 1903. 9½″ x 12″

311 Miss Newton. 1919. 9¾″ x 11½″

Herbert Barraud

Painter until the mid-sixties; thereafter portrait photographer in London. Published four volumes of celebrities entitled *Men and Women of the Day* 1888-1891.

312 Cardinal Newman. 1887. Woodbury-type. 7⅛″ x 9¾″

Hippolyte Bayard, 1801-1887

A clerk in the French Ministry of Finance, Bayard made photographic experiments from 1837 onward, and after hearing of Daguerre's success redoubled his efforts and became independent inventor of a direct positive process on paper, 1839. This was intentionally played down by Arago in order not to prejudice his negotiations with the Government in connection with a pension for Daguerre. In June 1839 Bayard publicly exhibited 30 photographs, but Daguerre's were considered more perfect. In the following years Bayard worked with every photographic process in turn.

313 Garden scene. c. 1850. 5″ x 6¾″

A. Beato

Italian landscape and documentary photographer, in partnership with James Robertson (q.v.) 1856-57. They published, partly separately, partly together, series of views of Constantinople, Palestine, Egypt, and of Lucknow and Delhi shortly after the Indian Mutiny. Beato also photographed during the Opium War in China, 1858 and 1860.

314 The Siege of Lucknow. Part of the Chatter-Manzil Palace, occupied by a British garrison, was blown up by rebellious Sepoys on 25 September, 1857. (Rep. from an album of photographs by Robertson and Beato.)

315 The Siege of Lucknow. The Secundrabagh was the last bulwark of the rebellious Indian troops in Lucknow and was re-taken by British troops on 21 March, 1858. 2000 mutineers were shot down in the courtyard. (Rep. from an album of photographs by Robertson and Beato.)

Cecil Beaton, b. 1904

English fashion and theater photographer from 1928 onward, and for 25 years *Vogue's* leading photographer of fashion and celebrities. Today Beaton is active mainly as a designer of stage and film costumes and sets. Author of 18 books illustrated with his photographs or drawings.

316 Jean Cocteau. 1936. 6¼″ x 8¾″

317 Christian Bérard, with his painting of Cecil Beaton in the fireplace. c. 1937. 10″ x 10″

318 The old Metro station Les Invalides, with Jean Cocteau. 1937. 10″ x 10″

319 Wild flowers. c. 1938. 10″ x 8″

Francis Bedford, 1816-1894

Originally a lithographer, Bedford was one of the best-known landscape and architectural photographers of the mid-nineteenth century in England, and was commanded by Queen Victoria to accompany the Prince of Wales (later Edward VII) on his educational tour of the Middle East in 1862. 172 of Bedford's photographs taken on this journey were published the following year.

320 Gizeh, Egypt. 1862. 12″ x 9″

321 Gate of the seraglio of the Sultan's Palace Dolma Bagcheh. 1862. 12″ x 9″

322 Bishop Audley's Chapel, Hereford Cathedral. c. 1856. 9½″ x 11½″

Bertall, 1820-1882

(pseudonym of the Vicomte d'Arnoux)

Well-known Parisian caricaturist and book illustrator, also active for some years as a portrait photographer.

323 Félicien David, composer. c. 1865. Carbon print. 7½″ x 9½″

324 Paul de Kock, author. c. 1865. Carbon print. 7½″ x 9½″

Werner Bischof, 1916-1954

Swiss reportage photographer, working for the Swiss Magazine *Du, Paris Match, Life* and other magazines in many parts of the world from 1945 until his death in a motor accident in the Andes. Member of the Magnum group. Many of his finest photographs were published in *Japan* (1954), *Indios* (1956), *Unterwegs* (1957).

325 Floods in East Hungary. 1947. 12″ x 15¾″

326 Famine in Madras, South India. 1951. 12″ x 15¾″

327 Shinto priests in the courtyard of the Meiji Temple, Tokyo. 1952. 14¼″ x 12″

328 Stepping-stones through the pond in the Heian Garden, Kyoto. 1952. 12″ x 15¾″

Louis and Auguste Bisson,
known as
Bisson Frères

b. 1814 and 1826 respectively. The Bisson brothers began as daguerreotypists in Paris in 1841 and were leading architectural photographers during the collodion period, and equally noted for their Alpine photographs. In July 1861 Auguste Bisson took the first photographs from the summit of Mont Blanc on an expedition lasting three days and requiring 25 porters to carry his apparatus, chemicals, and darktent.

329 Mont Blanc from the Grands Mulets. July, 1861. 9¾″ x 6½″

330 In the Savoy Alps. c. 1860. 17½″ x 12″

331 The Temples of Vespasian and Saturn in the Forum Romanum. c. 1860. 17½″ x 14¼″

332 Architrave of the Temple of Vespasian, c. 1860. 13½″ x 17½″

333 View from the mole, Venice, with S. Maria della Salute. c. 1860. 17¾″ x 13¾″

334 The Leaning Tower, Pisa. c. 1860. 13½″ x 17″

A. & J. Bool

Professional photographers who worked for the Society for Photographing Relics of Old London in the 1870's and '80s.

335 The "Oxford Arms," an old coaching inn in London. 1875. Carbon print. 10″ x 8″

336 A quaint old street in London. 1877. Carbon print. 8″ x 10″

Samuel Bourne, 1834-1912

Born in Nottingham, Bourne took up photography in the mid-1850's. About 1860, he sought his fortune in India and became a partner in the firm founded by Shepherd in Simla in 1843 (later also in Calcutta). Bourne soon became famous for his photographs of the Himalayas taken on expeditions lasting several months and requiring up to sixty coolies to carry the wet collodion equipment and other baggage. In 1868 Bourne photographed at an altitude of 18,600 feet—a record until 1880.

337 The Dhul Canal, Cashmere. c. 1863. 11½" x 9¼"

338 The Scinde River. c. 1863. 11½" x 9¼"

339 Baramula, from the south side of the river Jhelum. c. 1863. 11½" x 9¼"

340 Colonnade of Hindu pillars at the Kootub near Delhi. c. 1863. 11¾" x 9¼"

Bill Brandt, b. 1905

Born in London, brought up in Germany, Brandt learned photography from Man Ray in Paris, 1929-30, opened a portrait studio there, but influenced by the work of Atget, Cartier-Bresson and Brassaï, changed to reportage and documentation. Settled in London in 1931 as free-lance. In recent years has also photographed landscapes and celebrities at home. Published *The English at Home* (1936), *A Night in London* (1938), *Camera in London* (1948), *Literary Britain* (1951), *Perspective of Nudes* (1961).

341 Out-of-work miner searching for coal. 1936. 10" x 8"

342 Child in slum. c. 1935. 10" x 8"

343 Halifax. c. 1935. 10" x 8"

344 Working class family in Madrid. c. 1935. 10" x 8"

C. Brasch

Portrait photographer in Leipzig.

345 Siegfried Wilhelm Dehn, composer. c. 1855. 5½" x 7"

346 Moritz Hauptmann, composer, c. 1855. 5½" x 6¾"

Brassaï, b. 1899

(pseudonym for Gyula Halász)

Born in Brasso, Hungary, Brassaï originally intended to be an artist, but settled in Paris as a journalist in 1924 and six years later changed over to photography. He became known for his photographs of Paris by night and "candid" pictures of Parisians in unguarded moments, which indicated the new possibilities of reportage photography with the miniature camera. Brassaï's books *Paris de Nuit, Camera in Paris* and *Fiesta in Seville* contain some of his best-known photographs.

347 Entrance to the Bal Tabarin, Paris. 1932. 7" x 9¼"

348 Bijou de Montmartre. 1932. 7" x 9¼"

349 Streetwalker in Paris. 1933. 9¼" x 12"

350 A rainy day in Paris. 1935. 9" x 11½"

351 A lovely dream. 1937. 7" x 9¼"

(All photographs are enlargements from 35 mm. film negatives)

Adolphe Braun, 1811-1877

Born in Alsace, Braun began as a daguerreotypist c. 1842 and in the 1860's was famous for his instantaneous street views of Paris and mountain and landscape photographs in Switzerland. He founded the firm Braun & Cie. in Dornach and Paris (now Editions Braun) and introduced into France the carbon process particularly for the reproduction of paintings.

352 Panorama of Thun, Switzerland. 1867. Carbon print. 17¾" x 8¾"

353 Panorama of Interlaken, Switzerland. 1867. Carbon print. 17¾" x 8¾"

354 Panorama of Zürich, Switzerland. 1867. Carbon print. 17¾" x 8¾"

355 A Paris boulevard. c. 1860. Enl. rep. of a stereoscopic photograph.

J. Bridson

English amateur photographer.

356 Picnic. 1882. 8¾" x 6½"

Henry Herschel Hay Cameron

The youngest son of Julia Margaret Cameron had a studio in London from c. 1885-1905. In style his portraits are similar to those by his mother; technically they are considerably better though lacking perhaps the depth of her finest work.

357 Sir Henry Irving as Thomas Becket. 1893. 13¾" x 16¾"

Julia Margaret Cameron, 1815-1879

The wife of a retired member of the Council of India, Mrs. Cameron took up photography at the age of 48. Moving in intellectual circles, she had opportunities of photographing many famous Victorians whom she got to know through her friends and neighbors Alfred Tennyson and G. F. Watts, or through her sister who had a well-known salon. Many of Mrs. Cameron's striking portraits are artistically superior to the painted ones of the same sitters. Her close-ups, which were decades in advance of the time, bring out the soul of the individual. They are brilliant achievements surpassing even the fine portraits of Hill and Adamson. Unfortunately, Mrs. Cameron was persuaded by her artist friends to compose painterly and allegorical subjects unsuitable in the realistic medium of photography. These were highly praised by her contemporaries, but appear to us as errors of taste.

358 Sir Henry Taylor, poet. October, 1867. 10¾" x 13½"

359 Alfred, Lord Tennyson. 3 June, 1869. 9¼" x 11½"

360 Mrs. Herbert Duckworth. March, 1866. 11¼" x 13½"

361 Mrs. Herbert Duckworth. 1867. 10¼" x 12½"

362 "The Mountain Nymph, Sweet Liberty." June, 1866. 11" x 14¼"

363 "Ophelia." c. 1867. Dedicated to Dante Gabriel Rossetti. 11" x 13¾"

364 Jacques Blumenthal, composer. c. 1867. 9" x 11¼"

365 Edward John Eyre, diplomat. 4 June, 1867. 10" x 12¼"

366 Sir John Herschel, astronomer. 1867. 10¼" x 13½"

367 Sir John Herschel. 1867. 9½" x 12¾"

368 Thomas Carlyle. 1867. 9¼" x 12"

369 Unknown woman. c. 1868. 10" x 12½"

370 William Gifford Palgrave, explorer. 1868. 10" x 13¼"

371 Henry Wadsworth Longfellow. 1868. 10" x 13¾"

372 Joseph Joachim. April, 1868. 10" x 13"

373 Marie Spartali, a Greek beauty. March, 1868. 10¼" x 13½"

374 Charles Darwin. 1869. 9" x 11"

375 George Frederick Watts. 1868. 11" x 14"

376 Florence Fisher. 1872. 9¾" x 13"

377 "Florence." (Florence Fisher). August, 1872. 10¾" x 13¾". G. F. Watts, then the leading painter in Great Britain, wrote beneath this photograph: "I wish I could paint such a picture as this."

378 "The Angel at the Holy Sepulchre." c. 1872. 10¾" x 14½"

379 "Alethea" (Alice Liddell, the original *Alice in Wonderland*). 1872. 9¼" x 13" Carbon print from original negative.

380 Thomas Woolner, sculptor. c. 1870. 10¼" x 12¾"

381 A young girl with flower. c. 1868. 10⅝" x 14"

382 May Prinsep, a Pre-Raphaelite study. c. 1870. 10¾" x 13½". (rep.)

383 Ellen Terry. 1864. 12" circle.

Etienne Carjat, 1828-1906

Parisian caricaturist, writer, and editor of *Le Boulevard* 1862-3, Carjat also photographed celebrities during the years 1855-c. 1875. His portraits of celebrities are often livelier than Nadar's and have been undeservedly overshadowed by the latter's great reputation. Nos. 386 and 387 and some others are unrivalled in any artistic field.

384 Léon Gambetta, statesman. c. 1865. Carbon print. 7½" x 9½"

385 Jacques Halévy, composer. c. 1865. Carbon print. 7½" x 9½"

386 Gioachino Rossini. c. 1865. Carbon print. 7½" x 9½"

387 Charles Baudelaire. c. 1865. Carbon print. 7½" x 9½"

388 Alexandre Dumas. c. 1865. Carbon print. 7½″ x 9″

389 Frédéric Lemaître, actor. c. 1865. Carbon print. 7½″ x 9½″

Lewis Carroll, 1832-1898

(pseudonym for Rev. Charles Lutwidge Dodgson).

Author of *Alice's Adventures in Wonderland, Alice Through the Looking Glass* and other children's books, and mathematical lecturer at Christ Church, Oxford. The rediscovery of Lewis Carroll's photographic work and the publication of his diary entries by Helmut Gernsheim prove that photography was his chief hobby during the period 1856-1880. He was the best photographer of children in the nineteenth century, and also pursued celebrities with his camera.

390 Dante Gabriel Rossetti, Christina Rossetti with their mother and sister. 7 October, 1863. 10″ x 8″

391 Arthur Hughes, artist, and his daughter Agnes. 12 October, 1863. 7¾″ x 10″

392 "The Elopement" (Alice Jane Donkin). 9 October, 1862. 7½″ x 9¾″

393 Lewis Carroll's photograph album No. III containing 115 photographs of his child friends (mostly girls), and Victorian celebrities. Nearly every picture is signed by the sitter. The album is the finest of the ten surviving albums of Lewis Carroll, five of which are in the Gernsheim Collection. Nos. 394-404 are enlarged reproductions from this album.

394 Agnes Grace Weld. c. 1861.

395 Maria White. 1864.

396 Madeline Catherine Parnell. 1864.

397 Alice Constance Westmacott. 1864.

398 Aileen Wilson-Todd. 1865.

399 Ella Monier-Williams. 1866.

400 Hallam Tennyson. 1857.

401 Beatrice Henley. 1862.

402 Irene MacDonald. 1863.

403 Arthur Hughes. 1863.

404 Effie Millais. 1865.

405 Lewis Carroll's photograph album No. VI containing 70 photographs, chiefly of the Dodgson family and friends. Inscribed by him "Begun July, 1856," it is his first album in spite of its number. The album is opened to show Lewis Carroll's poem to Alice Murdoch and her portrait.

405 (a) Unnumbered photograph album by Lewis Carroll containing 76 photographs, chiefly of the Dodgson family and friends. Same period as No. 405.

Henri Cartier-Bresson, b. 1908

Leading French reportage photographer. Studied painting with André Lhôte in Paris, but changed over to reportage photography in 1930. From 1936-1939 he was assistant to the film director Jean Renoir and also made documentary films during the Spanish Civil War. During World War II Cartier-Bresson took an active part in the resistance movement. Since then he has traveled all over the world for the Magnum group which he founded in 1947. *Images à la Sauvette* is the finest of the many books illustrated with his photographs.

406 Children in Seville. 1933. 15½″ x 12″

407 Mexican prostitute. 1934. 12″ x 15½″

408 Sunday on the banks of the Marne. 1938. 15½″ x 12″

409 Cardinal Pacelli (later Pope Pius XII) before the Church Sacré-Coeur de Montmartre, Paris. 1938. 15½″ x 12″

410 Henri Matisse with a model. 1947. 12″ x 15½″

(All photographs are enlargements from 35 mm. negatives)

Winifred Casson, b. 1900

English photographer active in London in the 1930's.

411 "Accident" (double exposure). c. 1935. 9½″ x 11½″

412 Surrealistic composition. c. 1935. 6″ x 8″

Military School of the Royal Engineers, Chatham

The following photographs presaging the New Objectivity style of the 1920's were classwork of the Military School at Chatham, where from 1856 onward photography was taught to officers and sergeants of the Royal Engineers. Two years later a similar course was started for officers of the Royal Artillery at Woolwich.

413   Leaves in a wood. c. 1860. 8½″ x 6¾″

414   Dead tree in Windsor Forest. c. 1860. 14½″ x 11¼″

415   Old oak in Windsor Forest. c. 1860. 11½″ x 14¼″

Charles Clifford, ?-1863

English by birth, Clifford became Court photographer to Queen Isabella II of Spain, having taken up photography in the early 1850's. He is chiefly known for his large views depicting the beauty of Spanish architecture and scenery, and the Treasure of the Dauphin now at the Prado Museum. Published several albums of photographs, including *Vistas del Capricho,* 1856, and *Voyage en Espagne,* 1858.

416   Burgos Cathedral. c. 1855. 12″ x 15¾″

Alvin Langdon Coburn, b. 1882

Leading American amateur photographer, living in North Wales since 1918. After beginning art studies in Boston, Coburn changed over to photography and was a founder member of the Photo-Secession in 1902. His "impressionistic" portraits of English and French celebrities published under the title *Men of Mark* 1913 made Coburn known to a wider circle. He illustrated Henry James' *Novels and Tales* (1909) and published collectors' editions of hand-made photogravures of his pictures of New York (1910), London (1914) and others. In 1915 Coburn arranged at the Albright Art Gallery, Buffalo, the first exhibition of the British classics of photography. Coburn took the first purely abstract photograph in January, 1917. After the publication of *More Men of Mark* (1922) he gradually retired from photography.

417   St. Paul's Cathedral, London. 1908. Hand-made photogravure. 11¼″ x 15″

418   Water reflections. 1908. Hand-made photogravure. 15½″ x 11″

419   The island of Machen, Holland. 1908. Hand-made photogravure. 15½″ x 11″

420   "Vortograph" — the first abstract photograph. January, 1917. 6″ x 8¼″. Photographed through an arrangement of three mirrors forming a triangle.

Dr. Collot

Staff doctor of the cruiser H.M.S. "Collingwood."

421   Sinking of the battleship H.M.S. "Victoria" on 22 June, 1893. Enl. rep. Original size 8″ x 6″

During the summer manoeuvres of the British Mediterranean fleet, owing to an error of judgment on the part of Vice Admiral of the Fleet Sir George Tryon, the battleship "Camperdown" collided with the flagship "Victoria." "Victoria," the heaviest armed warship of the British Navy, sank within 15 minutes with half her complement of 718 men, including the Vice Admiral.

Howard Coster, 1885-1959

A South African, Coster had a portrait studio in Johannesburg from 1904 until 1924; then settled in London where he was noted for his portraits of famous men until his retirement in 1956.

422   G. K. Chesterton. 1928. 9¾″ x 11¼″

423   W. B. Yeats. c. 1930. 10″ x 12″

424   W. Somerset Maugham. 1930. 10″ x 12″

Philip H. Delamotte, 1820-1889

(For biography see p. 25)

425   Start of the rebuilding of the Crystal Palace at Sydenham, South London. Winter, 1853. 12″ x 9½″

426   Mid-day break of the constructional workers on the Crystal Palace. 1854. 12″ x 9½″

427   Opening of the rebuilt Crystal Palace by Queen Victoria on 10 June 1854. The Queen, Prince Albert, the whole royal family and the King of Portugal can be seen on the dais. This is the first instantaneous photograph of an historic occasion and was taken while everyone stood still during the

Archbishop of Canterbury's prayer. In the background is the orchestra and mixed choir of 1800 who performed Handel's Hallelujah Chorus. Slightly enlarged rep. of the original 8″ x 10″

428 Visit of Napoleon III, the Empress Eugénie, Queen Victoria, and Prince Albert to the Crystal Palace on 20 April 1855. During the Crimean War the alliance of England and France was strengthened by State visits of both sovereigns. 7¾″ x 5¾″

429 Interior of the Crystal Palace. 1859. 9¼″ x 11½″

430 View of the Crystal Palace from the garden. 1859. (Enl. rep.)

Robert Demachy, ?-1938

Banker and influential French amateur photographer, who perfected the gum print (1894). By the addition of various pigments the photograph could be given the appearance of a red chalk or charcoal drawing, and an impressionistic effect could be obtained by handwork on the negative. The aesthetic movement in photography was a reaction against the mass productions of inartistic amateur snapshooters.

431 "Primavera." 1898. Photo etching of a gum print. 6″ x 8½″

432 Behind the scenes. 1904. Photogravure of a gum print. (rep.)

André Adolphe Disdéri, 1819-c.1890

French Court photographer; patented in 1854 the carte-de-visite. Several (usually eight) small portraits were taken on one plate and the print cut up into the single pictures. By this mass-production method the price of each photograph was considerably reduced. Carte-de-visite photographs only became fashionable in 1859 after Napoleon III had his portrait taken by Disdéri in this format. They were not used as visiting cards, but portraits of well-known people were published in thousands, collected in albums, and exchanged like stamps. A few years later photograph albums were sometimes fitted with musical boxes. Disdéri soon became the richest photographer in the world, with an income of £48,000 a year from his Paris studio alone. He also had branches in London, Toulon, and Madrid. Disdéri dissipated his fortune and ended in the poor-house at Nice.

433 Sheet of 8 uncut carte-de-visite portraits of Cardinal de la Vigerie. c. 1862. 9½″ x 8″

434 Carte-de-visite album with musical box playing two tunes. c. 1868. 9½″ x 11¾″. Moulded plastic cover in high relief with design of the balcony scene in "Romeo and Juliet."

Henry Dixon

London photographer active for the Society for Photographing Relics of Old London in the 1870's and '80's.

435 Old houses in London's dockland. 1881. Carbon print. 8″ x 10″

Edward Draper

English amateur photographer.

436 Boy with parrot. c. 1865. Enl. rep.

Harold E. Edgerton, b. 1903

Born Fremont, Nebraska, Edgerton, an engineer, began high-speed photographic experiments in 1930. The following year invented an electronic flashlamp with which it is possible to analyze the fastest movements in a series of stroboscopic photographs, or to record the whole movement on one film. Since 1936 Edgerton has been professor at Massachusetts Institute of Technology.

437 Splash of milk resulting from a drop of milk which has fallen onto a plate of milk. A second drop is seen falling. Exposure 1/100,000,000 second at F.64. 1936. 8″ x 10″

438 Baton-thrower. 1936. 10″ x 8″

439 Golfer. (Dennis Shute) 1935. 10″ x 8″

(All are enlargements from 35mm. negatives)

Edmiston

English advertising photographer in the 'thirties, active in London.

440 Solarization. c. 1934. 10¼″ x 14¼″

441 Solarization. c. 1934. 11″ x 14½″

Peter Henry Emerson, 1856-1936

American by birth, Emerson became a doctor in England but gave up this career in order to devote himself to writing and photography, having been an amateur since 1882. In reaction against the stagnant artificialities of conventional Salon photography, Emerson founded the "school" of naturalistic photography. Published seven photographically illustrated books of landscapes in limited editions with platinotypes or photo-etchings. In photography Emerson played a similar role to that of Courbet in painting.

442 Taking up the eel net. 1885.

443 Gunner working up to fowl. 1885.

444 During the reed harvest. 1885.

445 Gathering water lilies. 1885.

446 Setting the bow-net. 1885.

(Nos. 442-446 are somewhat enlarged reproductions of platinotypes, 11½″ x 7½″, in Emerson's book *Life and Landscape on the Norfolk Broads*. London 1886. See No. 867.)

447 A winter's morning. 1886. Photogravure. 11¼″ x 7″

448 A spring idyl. 1886. Photogravure. 7¼″ x 10¼″

449 Going to market. 1886. Photogravure. 10¼″ x 8¾″

450 A fisherman at home. 1886. Photogravure. 9″ x 9½″

(Nos. 447-450 are from Emerson's book *Pictures from Life in Field and Fen,* London, 1887.)

451 Haymaker with rake. 1887. Photogravure. 8″ x 11″

452 A stiff pull. 1887. Photogravure. 11¼″ x 8¼″

453 In the barley harvest. 1887. Photogravure. 9¾″ x 9¼″

(Nos. 451-453 are plates from Emerson's book *Pictures of East Anglian Life,* London, 1888.)

454 Winter landscape. 1891. Photo-etching. 6½″ x 4″

(Plate from Emerson's book *On English Lagoons,* London, 1893.)

455 Winter landscape. 1894. Photo-etching. 5¾″ x 4″

(Plate from Emerson's book *Marsh Leaves,* London, 1895.)

William England, ?-1896

Originally a portrait photographer with the daguerreotype process, in the 1850's and '60's England became one of Britain's leading landscape photographers. He made thousands of pictures on his journeys, which took him, among other places, to America. England was particularly known for his photographs of Switzerland, the Tyrol and Italy.

456 Album entitled *Panoramic Views of Switzerland, Savoy and Italy.* c. 1864. Contains 77 original photographs 6½″ x 3½″

457 The island San Giulio in Lake Orta. c. 1864. Enl. rep. from this album.

458 The railway bridge over the Niagara River. 1859. Enl. rep. of a stereoscopic photograph.

Hugo Erfurth, 1874-1948

Leading German portrait photographer active in Dresden 1896-1934 and in Cologne 1934-1943. A great supporter of the aesthetic movement in Germany, Erfurth made only gum prints, and later oil pigment prints. In the 1920's he was the most celebrated portrait photographer of the German intelligentsia.

459 A young woman. 1898. 11½″ x 13¼″

460 Negative print of a lady with large hat. c. 1910. 11¾″ x 15½″

461 Oskar Kokoschka. 1919. 7½″ x 10¼″

462 Käthe Kollwitz. c. 1925 8¾″ x 11¼″

463 Gerhardt Hauptmann. c. 1925. 22″ x 26″

464 Walter Gropius c. 1927. 7¾″ x 10¼″

465 Otto Julius Bierbaum. c. 1920. 17¼″ x 23″

466 Wassily Kandinsky. c. 1926. 8¾″ x 11¼″

466 (a) Portrait of a dancer. c. 1928. 11½″ x 15½″

Frederick H. Evans, 1852-1943

A bookdealer by profession, Evans was, like his friend G. Bernard Shaw, an enthusiastic amateur photographer. He turned professional in 1898, taking photographs of English cathedrals and French châteaux. He also took portraits of a number of his literary and artistic friends, including G. B. Shaw and Aubrey Beardsley whom he set on his career as an illustrator. Evans worked with large plates and only made contact copies on platinotype paper. When this paper became unobtainable during World War I he gave up photography.

467 Edward the Confessor's Chapel, Westminster Abbey. 1911. Modern contact copy from original negative. 8″ x 10″

468 East ambulatory, Westminster Abbey. 1911. Modern contact copy from original negative. 8″ x 10″

469 Château de Chambord, France. c. 1913. Modern contact copy from original negative. 8½″ x 10¾″

Walker Evans, b. 1903

American professional photographer since 1930, now associate editor of *Fortune*. Famous for his photo-documentation of the impoverished Southern States taken 1935-36 for the Farm Security Administration, which shocked by their outspokenness. Some of the most striking were published under the title *American Photographs* by the Museum of Modern Art, New York.

470 Garage on the outskirts of a Southern city. 1936.

471 Country store and gas station, Alabama. 1936.

472 Negro church, South Carolina. 1936.

473 Sharecropper's family. Alabama. 1936.

474 Sidewalk in Vicksburg, Mississippi. 1936.

(The above photographs are enlargements from the original negatives at the Library of Congress.)

Roger Fenton, 1819-1869

Fenton first came into contact with photography while studying painting in Paris under Paul Delaroche in the 1840's. Later he became a barrister in London, but was more interested in photography and was for eleven years exclusively active as a photographer. In 1862 he returned to his legal profession. Fenton made outstanding architectural and landscape photographs, but is most famous for his photographs of the Crimean War — the first photographic war reportage. He was also founder of the Photographic Society of London (now the Royal Photographic Society of Great Britain) in 1853 — the oldest society still in existence. The following photographs are all Calotype prints from collodion negatives.

475 A quiet day at the mortar battery. 1855. 13¾″ x 9¾″

476 Ismail Pasha and attendants. 1855. 6¼″ x 7½″

477 The Sanitary Commission: Dr. John Sutherland and Sir Robert Rawlinson. 1855. 6¼″ x 7¾″

478 Camp life: Roger Fenton and his two assistants. 1855. 6½″ x 7″

479 Lieut. General Sir George Brown and staff. 1855. 6½″ x 6¾″

480 Lieut. Col. Brownrigg and two captured Russian boys. 1855. 6½″ x 6¾″

481 Officers of the 71st Highlanders. 1855. 6½″ x 7¼″

482 Council of War of the allied Commanders-in-Chief: Lord Raglan, Omar Pasha, and General Pélissier. 1855. 6½″ x 7½″

483 The cattle pier, Balaclava. 1855. 14½″ x 11″

484 Lieut. General Sir George de Lacy Evans. 1855. 6¼″ x 7½″

485 Field kitchen of the 8th Hussars. 1855. 8″ x 6¼″

486 General Bosquet and Captain Dampière. 1855. 6″ x 7¾″

487 Ruined Genoese fort, Balaclava harbor. 1855. 14½″ x 11″

488 Camp of the 4th Dragoons. 1855. 8½″ x 6¼″

489 The head of Balaclava harbor. 1855. 14¼″ x 11½″

490 Lieut. General Sir John Campbell and Captain Hume. 1855. 6″ x 7¾″

491 Cavalry camp, Balaclava. 1855. 14″ x 10¾″

492 Lieut. General Sir H. J. W. Bentinck. 1855. 6¼″ x 7½″

493 Encampment of Horse Artillery. 1855. 14″ x 11″

494 Balaclava harbor. 1855. 14″ x 11½″

Francis Frith, 1822-1898

English landscape photographer, and Europe's largest publisher of topographical views. Illustrated a large number of books with his photographs, including Longfellow's *Hyperion* (No. 858a). Frith's finest pictures were taken on three journeys to Egypt, Palestine and Syria 1856-1860. He worked under the greatest difficulties, penetrating by boat, horse and camel 1500 miles up the Nile. The temperature in his dark-tent often rose to 120-130°F. and the collodion frequently boiled when poured on the glass plate. Frith's contact copies show with what enormous plate sizes he and some other photographers worked at that period when enlarging was not a practicable proposition.

495 Temple of Philae. 1858. 19″ x 14½″. In the foreground is the boat in which Frith traveled up the Nile.

496 View of Cairo from the citadel. 1858. 19″ x 14½″

497 Temple of Kom-Umboo. 1858. 19″ x 14½″

498 The pyramids of Dahshoor. 1858. 19″ x 14½″

499 The pyramids of El Gizeh. 1858. 19″ x 14¾″

500 Mount Serbal. 1858. 19″ x 14½″

501 Mosque in Cairo. 1858. 14½″ x 19″

502 The great Pyramid and Sphinx. 1858. 19″ x 14½″

(Photographs from *Egypt, Sinai and Jerusalem*, London c. 1860. The text pages measure no less than 21″ x 29″.)

Alexander Gardner, 1821-1882

Scottish amateur photographer, emigrated with his family to America in 1856 and two years later was engaged by Mathew Brady as manager of his studio in Washington. During the Civil War Gardner was at the beginning on Brady's staff of war photographers, then for some months official photographer to the Army of the Potomac; later he commissioned other photographers to take war photographs for him as well. In 1865 Gardner published a hundred of these photographs in two albums (see No. 859) from which the following pictures have been abstracted: Nos. 503, 660, 661, 806-8.

503 President Lincoln visits the Army of the Potomac 1-5 October 1862. Facing him is General McLellan. 10″ x 8″

504 Execution of the conspirators against Lincoln in the courtyard of the Washington Penitentiary. 7 July 1865. (rep.)

De Gaston

French amateur photographer active in China before World War II. He used a miniature camera, and toned his enlargements sepia.

505 A Chinese monk. c. 1932. 15″ x 11″

506 An old Chinese workman. c. 1932. 15″ x 11″

507 A water-taxi. c. 1932. 15″ x 11″

508 Washerwomen at the river's edge. c. 1932. 15″ x 11″

509 The public writer. c. 1932. 15″ x 11″

510 A boat. c. 1932. 15″ x 11″

Dr. Arnold Genthe, 1868-1942

After obtaining a Dr. Phil. degree in Jena, Genthe emigrated to San Francisco in 1895. He photographed as a hobby, then two years later made photography his profession and became a successful society portrait photographer. In 1911 Genthe opened a studio in New York. His most interesting pictures are those made in Chinatown, San Francisco, while still an amateur, and his documentation of the earthquake on 18 April 1906. Genthe published *Pictures of Old Chinatown* and his autobiography *As I Remember*.

511 An aristocrat of Chinatown. 1895.

512 Street of the Gamblers, Chinatown. 1895.

513 Emergency feeding of homeless after the San Francisco earthquake. 1906.

514 San Francisco after the earthquake and fire. 1906.

(All 10″ x 8″ enlargements from Genthe's original negatives in the California Palace of the Legion of Honor, San Francisco.)

D. S. George

English photographer and official photo-reporter of the construction of the Assuan Dam in Egypt, 1900-1902.

515 The Assuan Dam during a solar eclipse on 11 November 1901. Platinotype. 11½″ x 9½″.

Helmut Gernsheim, b. 1913

Author, collector, and photo-historian.

Forced by conditions in Germany, Gernsheim changed over from the study of art history to photography in 1934, and studied at the Bavarian State School of Photography in Munich. In 1937 he settled in London where he made a name with his objective portraits, architectural and sculptural photographs. During the war he photographed historic buildings and monuments in London, taking thousands of detail photographs for the Warburg Institute in collaboration with the National Buildings Record. Since 1945 Gernsheim has built up what constitutes today the largest photo-historical collection in the world, and has written — in some cases in collaboration with his wife — 17 books on photo-historical and general historical subjects. Awarded German cultural prize for photography 1959.

516 Skeleton of a leaf. 1937. Enlargement from a 3½″ x 4¾″ negative.

517 Open-air portrait. 1935. Enlargement from a 2¼″ x 2¼″ negative.

518 Piano hammers. 1936. Enlargement from a 3½″ x 4¾″ negative.

519 New housing estate. 1937. Enlargement from 2¼″ x 2¼″ negative.

520 Section through cucumber. 1936. Enlargement from 3½″ x 4¾″ negative.

521 Portrait in Stone (monument in St. Margaret's, Westminster). 1943. Enlargement from 3½″ x 4¾″ negative.

Maurice Guibert

French amateur photographer and representative of a champagne firm. Constant companion of Toulouse-Lautrec in his night-life, Guibert sat to the painter for "À la Mie" and other canvases, and himself painted, referring to himself as "the pupil of God and Toulouse-Lautrec." Toulouse-Lautrec, recognizing the originality of Guibert's photographs, frequently made use of them for his lithographs and paintings.

522 Henri de Toulouse-Lautrec. 1896. The first close-up. 8″ x 10″

523 Toulouse-Lautrec asleep at the Château de Malromé. 1896. 10″ x 8″

(Enlargements from photographs in the collection of the late Ludwig Charell.)

Miroslav Hák

Czechoslovak professional photographer active in Prague.

524 Rain. 1936. 11¾″ x 15½″

525 In the courtyard. 1943. 11¾″ x 15½″

Arno Hammacher, b. 1927

Dutch typographer and industrial photographer in Milan. Studied at the Art Academy in The Hague 1950-53 and was then for four years graphic designer in a typefoundry. Published in 1954 a photographic study entitled: *Van Gogh, the land where he was born and raised.*

526 Reflections. 1951. 12″ x 9½″

527 Detail picture from a photo-documentation of Naum Gabo's monument in Rotterdam. 1957. 11¾″ x 15¾″

528 Another detail photograph. 11¾″ x 15¾″

Hans Hammarskiöld, b. 1925

Swedish professional photographer active in Stockholm. A pupil of Rolf Winquist and then assistant to Bellander. From 1954-1956 Hammarskiöld was staff photographer of *Vogue* in London. Since then he is a freelance fashion and advertising photographer in Stockholm, and a member of the Swedish group "Tio." Published *Objektivt Sett,* 1955.

529 Section through a tree-trunk. 1951. 11¾″ x 15¾″

530 Bark of a tree. 1952. 11¾″ x 15¾″

531 Frosty grass. 1952. 11″ x 13¾″

532 Air-bubbles in water. 1954. 11″ x 13¾″

533 A Lippizaner at the Spanish Riding School, Vienna. 1954. 12″ x 9″

Bert Hardy, b. 1913

English reportage and advertising photographer. Started as press photographer for a London news agency in 1937; served in the photographic division of the army in the Far East 1942-1946. For over ten years Hardy was chief photographer of *Picture Post* until its demise in 1957. Awarded the *Encyclopedia Britannica* prize for his reportage of the Korean War.

534 In Cashmere. 1947. 12″ x 10″

535 Beggar children in Barcelona. 1950. 10″ x 12″

536 Mother and child in Liverpool. 1951. 12″ x 10″

537 Story-teller during the wine harvest near Lyon. 1951. 12″ x 10″

John Havindon, b. 1908

Professional photographer in Australia, the United States and London until 1940. During the war Havindon made documentary films, and since then is active as an antique dealer.

538 Nude. c. 1935. 11″ x 13″

Viscountess Hawarden, 1822-1865

English amateur photographer noted for her photographs of children, which influenced Lewis Carroll.

539 At the window. c. 1864. Enl. rep. from Lewis Carroll's album of collected photographs.

Frederick Hollyer, 1837-1933

English portrait photographer and specialist in reproductions of paintings. Best known for his platinotype portraits of artists and authors taken in their own surroundings between 1890 and 1914.

540 Aubrey Beardsley, 1896. Enlargement from the original 4¾″ x 6½″ negative.

E. O. Hoppé, b. 1878

Born in Bavaria, Hoppé was for a time a bank clerk in London until he adopted photography as his profession in 1907. For the next twenty years he was the leading portrait photographer of intellectual society in London. From 1927 onward specialized in photographing places and people in all parts of the world and published a large series of illustrated books for *Orbis Terrarum,* including one on America.

541 Alice Meynell. 1908. 5½″ x 7¾″ contact print.

542 Brooklyn Bridge. 1919. 6½″ x 8½″

543 Ship in drydock. 1927. 11″ x 9″

544 Ambush. 1933. 8¼″ x 10¾″

Robert Howlett, ?-1858

English professional photographer. Made a set of photographs of Crimean War heroes for Queen Victoria, took some reportage pictures of Derby day for the artist W. P. Frith (1856) and of the launching of the "Great Eastern" steamship (1857).

545 I. K. Brunel, designer of the "Great Eastern," the largest ship of the nineteenth century. November 1857. 9″ x 11″

Alice Hughes

Photographer of English and Continental royalty and society women from c. 1887 until about 1925. Her fine platinotype prints are the epitome of an elegant age.

546 The Princess of Wales (later Queen Alexandra). c. 1889. Platinotype. 8¼″ x 11¼″

547 Archduchess Stephanie, widow of Crown Prince Rudolph of Hapsburg. c. 1905. Platinotype. 5¾″ x 8¼″

Kurt Hutton, 1893-1960

Born in Strasbourg, Hübschmann's law studies were interrupted by World War I. In 1923 he opened a photographic portrait studio, but six years later changed over to photo-reportage and worked for various German illustrated papers. Settled in England in 1934 under the name of Hutton. Staff photographer of *Picture Post* from its foundation in 1938 until 1955.

548 Unemployed. 1939. 11½″ x 14¾″

549 The white horse. 1939. 14″ x 11¼″

550 Girl at fun-fair. 1938. 11″ x 14¾″

551 Scenic railway. 1938. 11½″ x 14¾″

(All pictures are enlargements from 35 mm. negatives.)

James Jarché, b. 1890

London press photographer since 1907.

552 Policewoman chasing naked boys at the Serpentine, Hyde Park, c. 1925, before bathing was allowed there. 14½″ x 11½″

Baynham Jones, 1806-1890

English amateur photographer who worked with every process from the daguerreotype to gelatine dry plates.

553 "A Misty Morning." c. 1862. 9″ x 7½″

Ida Kar, b. 1908

Born near Moscow of Armenian parentage, opened a portrait studio in Cairo in 1940, settled in London in 1945 and has been a free-lance portrait photographer ever since. Noted for her portraits of famous artists, authors and musicians, begun in 1953.

554 Marc Chagall. 1954. 19″ x 15¼″ . .

555 Henry Moore. 1954. 17¼″ x 15¼″

556 Alberto Giacometti. 1954. 10″ x 12″

557 Dimitri Shostakovich. 1959. 10″ x 12″

Peter Keetman, b. 1916

German professional photographer. Studied at the Bavarian State School of Photography. After war service Keetman began his career as a free-lance photographer and became a founding member of *Fotoform* in 1949 (later called *Subjective Photography*). His fields of activity are chiefly topography, industry and advertising. Published several topographical books.

558 Oscillation photograph. 1950. 11¾″ x 15¾″

559 Washing on line. 1952. 15¾″ x 11¾″

560 Oil drops. 1956. 11¾″ x 15¾″

561 Self-portrait in a sieve. 1957. 11¾″ x 15¾″

562 Ice formations on a lake. 1958. 15¾″ x 11¾″

Heinrich Kühn, 1866-1944

Born in Dresden, after studying medicine settled in Innsbruck, Austria, in 1888, devoting himself entirely to photography in which he had been an amateur since 1879. Prominent exhibitor of portraits and landscapes, using the gum print, Kühn was, with Watzek and Henneberg one of the leaders of the aesthetic movement in photography in Austria. An honorary doctor's degree of Innsbruck University was conferred upon Kühn in 1937 for his work in furthering artistic photography.

563 Prof. Perathoner, sculptor. 1905. 9¼″ x 11½″

Dorothea Lange, b. 1895

American professional photographer; originally had a portrait studio in San Francisco. A member of the F.64 Group 1932. One of the team of photographers working in 1935-6 for the Farm Security Administration, Dorothea Lange documented the plight of migrant labor in California. John Steinbeck credits her photographs with inspiring his classic novel, *Grapes of Wrath*. Her books include *An American Exodus* (1939) and *The New California* (1957).

564 Migrant landworker's wife and children. 1936. 10½" x 13½"

565 Sharecropper. 1936. 10½" x 13½" (Enlargements from the original negatives at the Library of Congress.)

Clarence J. Laughlin, b. 1905

American landscape and architectural photographer since 1936. Particularly fascinated by the strange and fantastic, Laughlin was drawn to the beauty of the ruined architecture of New Orleans, his home town, and the abandoned cotton plantations of Louisiana. Selections of his poetical photographs were published in his books *Ghosts along the Mississippi* and *New Orleans and its Living Past*.

566 Three vistas through one wall. 1937. 13¾" x 10⅝"

567 "The unending stream." 1939. 13½" x 11"

568 "The Fierce-eyed Building." 1940. 10¼" x 13¾"

569 "Farewell to the Past." 1941. 10¼" x 13¼"

570 "Elegy for Moss Land." 1947. 13¾" x 10¾"

J. Laurent

Professional photographer in Madrid.

571 and 572 Bullfight. c. 1895. 13" x 9½"

Gustave Le Gray, 1820-1862

French painter, portrait and landscape photographer. Devised the waxed paper process (1851) and wrote a number of photographic manuals. In 1851 Le Gray took photographs for the French Government Commission for Historic Monuments. Famous for his instantaneous seascapes showing for the first time clouds in the sky (1856). His photographs probably influenced Courbet.

573 Notre-Dame, Paris. c. 1858. 16" x 20". In spite of its very large size this is a contact print, not an enlargement.

574 "Brig upon the water." 1856. 16½" x 12¾"

575 Seascape. 1856. 16½" x 12¾"

Helmar Lerski, 1871-1956

Born in Strasbourg, Lerski emigrated to the United States in 1893 and became an actor. His first wife, a professional portrait photographer in Milwaukee, persuaded him to change to photography in 1911. Four years later, an exhibition of his portraits in Berlin led to his engagement as cameraman for leading Berlin film companies. After the introduction of sound film Lerski returned to portrait photography, studying the creative effects of light in characterization. In 1931 he published *Köpfe des Alltags*—close-ups of simple people. The same year he emigrated to Palestine where he pursued his idea of "metamorphosis through light" in thousands of physiognomical studies of Jewish peasants and Arab laborers. The last eight years of his life were spent in Zurich. A large selection from his life's work was published in *Der Mensch-mein Bruder (Man —my Brother)* in 1958.

576 Metal-worker. 1931. 9" x 11½"

577 Washerwoman. 1931. 9" x 11½"

578 Bedouin. c. 1934. 9" x 11½"

579 Young Jewish porter. c. 1934. 9" x 11½"

580 An Arab. c. 1934. 9" x 11½" (All photographs are contact copies from 9½" x 12" plates.)

London Stereoscopic Company

Firm founded in 1854 for the sale of stereoscopes and binocular photographs, later extended their business to larger photographic prints.

581 Traffic in the Strand, London. c. 1890. (enl. rep.)

Dame Kathleen Lonsdale, F.R.S.

English scientist, head of the department of chemistry at University College, London.

582 X-ray diffraction photograph of a pentaerythritol crystal having tetragonal symmetry. 1960. 8" x 10"

Nahum Luboshez, 1869-1925

A Russian domiciled in England from 1894 onward, Luboshez worked at the Kodak Research Laboratories at Harrow near London. For some years before World War I he was Kodak's representative at St. Petersburg. An enthusiastic amateur photographer, Luboshez took chiefly portraits, including the well-known one of George Eastman (see No. 90). He did important research work on the improvement of X-ray film emulsions.

583 Famine in Russia. Two children. c. 1910. 13¾" x 12½"

584 Famine in Russia. A little girl. c. 1910. 13½" x 19"

585 Famine in Russia. Easter morning at the Kremlin. c. 1910. 17" x 13½"

586 Famine in Russia. Hay-making. c. 1910. 17¼" x 14"

Angus McBean, b. 1905

Leading London stage photographer since 1935. Influenced by surrealism, McBean combined fantasy with realism, and in his novel portraits of famous stage people in elaborate settings devised by himself, created original and astonishing effects.

587 Pamela Stanley as Queen Victoria. 1938. 16" x 20"

588 Peggy Ashcroft as Portia in *The Merchant of Venice*. 1938. 16" x 20"

589 Celia Johnson in *Rebecca*. 1939. 12" x 16"

(All enlargements from 4" x 5" negatives.)

Robert MacPherson, 1811-1872

Edinburgh surgeon, settled in Rome for health reasons in the early 1840's. Became a painter and art-dealer, and in 1851 took up photography. Within a few years MacPherson was the leading photographer of architecture, views, and Roman antiquities. His splendid large pictures of the principal classical sites and over 300 photographs of sculpture in the Vatican are unequalled by later photographers. Published a guide-book to the Vatican sculptures (1863). Devised a process of photolithography (1855).

590 Relief on the inside of the Arch of Titus, Rome. c. 1857. 11" x 14½"

591 Ditto, the opposite side. c. 1857. 11" x 14½"

592 Forum Romanum with Temple of Saturn. c. 1857. 16" x 12"

593 The Cascades at Tivoli. c. 1857. 15¾" x 12"

594 View of Rome from the Monte Gianicolo. c. 1857. 15¼" x 8"

595 Trajan's Column and the church of S. Nome di Maria. c. 1858. 12½" x 16¾"

596 Cloisters of the Basilica di S. Paolo. c. 1858. 14½" x 11¼"

597 The Piazza del Popolo. c. 1858. 15½" x 12"

598 St. Peter's and the Vatican. c. 1860. 14½" x 10½"

599 View from the Pincio, with St. Peters. c. 1860. 9½" x 5¾"

600 Temple of Antoninus Pius and Faustina in the Forum Romanum. c. 1857. 11" x 15"

601 In the garden of the Villa d'Este, Tivoli. c. 1857. 12" x 15½"

602 The Cloaca Maxima. 1856. 14" x 9½"

603 Church of S. Maria Maggiore. c. 1856. 16" x 12½"

604 St. Peter's and the Castel S. Angelo. c. 1860. 14¾" x 9"

605 "Temple of Vesta" and baroque fountain. c. 1860. 15¾" x 11"

606 The Piazza Barberini. c. 1856. 15½" x 12"

607 The sculpture gallery in the Vatican. c. 1858. 12½" x 13½"

608 The Villa d'Este, Tivoli. c. 1857. 10¾" x 13¾"

609 Roman pine-trees. c. 1857. 12" x 15½"

610 Church of St. Francis, Assisi. c. 1858. 15" x 12"

Felix H. Man, b. 1893
(Pseudonym for Hans Baumann)

German by birth, Man was originally a sports illustrator for a Berlin newspaper before taking up miniature photography in 1928. He became a pioneer in photo-journalism, working for the Munich and Berlin illustrated weeklies. Man made reportages of social and general interest events by available light, and had photo-interviews with many famous people. Pioneered a new kind of picture story with *A Day with Mussolini* (1931). Settled in London in 1934, worked for *Illustrated,* and was chief photographer to *Picture Post* from its foundation in 1938 until 1945. Took for *Life* the first reportage in color by night, of the Festival of Britain, 1951. Retired in 1953. Published *150 Years of Artists' Lithographs* (1953) and *Eight European Artists* (1954).

611   Aristide Briand and his private secretary at the Quai d'Orsay. 1930. Enlargement from 1¾" x 2¼" negative.

612   Igor Stravinsky conducting at a rehearsal. 1929. Taken by daylight. Enlargement from 1¾" x 2¼" negative.

613   Pablo Casals playing. 1929. Taken by candle-light. Enlargement from 1¾" x 2¼" negative.

614   Trombones. 1929. Enlargement from 1¾" x 2¼" negative.

615   Steelworks. 1939. Enlargement from 35 mm. negative.

616   A tramp. 1939. Enlargement from 35 mm. negative.

Paul Martin, 1864-1942

English wood engraver for newspaper illustrations, and amateur photographer from 1884 onward. Martin's snapshots of London street life and of people enjoying themselves at the seaside, taken in the 1890's with a hand camera hidden in a brief case, make him the first "candid cameraman" in the world. His series of London by night (actually taken in twilight), 1896 were also the first of their kind and caused a sensation. From 1900 to 1908 Martin worked as a press photographer in London; thereafter joined a firm of photoengravers.

617   Yarmouth beach. 1892.

618   Audience at a seaside concert party. 1892.

(Enl. rep. from original negatives 3¼" x 4¼".)

Maull & Polyblank

London firm of portrait photographers from 1855 to 1880. In the late 'fifties they issued a large series of fine portraits of the distinguished members of learned societies and other celebrities.

619   Michael Faraday. 1856.

620   W. E. Gladstone. c. 1856.

(Enl. rep. from Lewis Carroll's album of collected photographs. Original size 5¼" x 6¾")

John Edwin Mayall, 1810-1901
(see also Nos. 115-118)

A daguerreotypist in Philadelphia from 1842 to 1846, Mayall opened a portrait studio in the Strand, London, early in 1847, and was a leading portraitist for three decades. Mayall introduced into England the albumen on glass process in 1851, and was quick to realize the potentialities of the carte-de-visite portrait made popular by Disdéri of Paris. Mayall's carte portraits of the English royal family taken in May, 1860, and published as *The Royal Album,* started the craze for the carte-de-visite and for photograph albums, and made Mayall the richest photographer in Britain. He earned £12,000 a year (then $48,000). In 1866 Mayall left the management of his London studio to his sons and opened a new establishment at Brighton, of which town he was elected mayor in 1877.

621   *The Royal Album.* Red morocco album 5¼" x 6". 1860. Containing 14 carte photographs of Queen Victoria and her family taken in May, 1860. Printed title and contents pages.

Laszlo Moholy-Nagy, 1895-1947

Hungarian painter and photographer; founder and director of the photographic department at the Bauhaus, 1923-1928. Made first photograms in 1922. Published two Bauhaus books, *Malerei, Photographie, Film* (1925) and *Von Malerei zu Architektur* (1929). Also made a number of films between 1926-1935. In 1934 Moholy-Nagy moved to Amsterdam, the following year to London. From 1937 until his death he was director of the School of Design in Chicago, which he had founded.

622 Photogram. 1922. One of his first abstract photographs. 7″ x 9¼″

623 Nude. Negative print. c. 1935. 10¾″ x 14¾″

624 Looking down from the radio tower, Berlin. 1928. 11½″ x 14¾″

Raymond Moore, b. 1920

English photographer. War service interrupted Moore's training as a designer and painter, which he completed at the Royal College of Art, London, 1947-50. After that, teacher of lithography and painting at Watford School of Art near London until 1957. Though for many years interested in photography, Moore's serious activity in this field dates only from 1957 when he was appointed teacher of photography at the Watford School. At first he took landscapes, but gradually the painter's predilection for pure form and design led him to concentrate more and more on abstract patterns found in nature and in man-made objects.

625 "Sleeping Rock." 1961.

626 "Flowers of Decay—Ceiling." 1961.

627 "Wall of Light." 1961.

628 "Interior Enigma." 1961.

629 "No Entry." 1961.

630 "Snowbound." 1961.

All photographs are enlargements from 2¼″ x 2¼″ negatives.

James Mudd

Took up photography soon after the introduction of the collodion process and was a professional portraitist in Manchester. His reputation today rests chiefly on his brilliant landscapes made for exhibitions. Author of a small handbook on photography, 1866.

631 Floods at Sheffield. 1864. 14¾″ x 11″

Mulnier

Professional portrait photographer in Paris.

632 Charles Gounod. c. 1868. Carbon print. 7½″ x 9½″

Eadweard Muybridge, 1830-1904

Born at Kingston-on-Thames near London, Muybridge emigrated to California in 1852, where he took up photography a few years later, working for a time with the explorer and photographer Watkins. Muybridge's photographic activity is first mentioned in 1867 in connection with his views of the Yosemite Valley. The following year he photographed in Alaska for the government on an official survey; later on became chief photographer to the U. S. government. In the 'seventies he took hundreds of views for the Central and South Pacific Railway Company and for the Pacific Mail Steamship Company. It was generally admitted that Muybridge's magnificent views made the beauties of America better known than had ever been done before by pen or pencil.

633 El Capitan, Yosemite. 1872. 20½″ x 15½″

634 The upper Yosemite waterfall. 1872. 15½″ x 20½″

635 The lower Yosemite waterfall. 1872. 15½″ x 20½″

636 The Columbia River, Oregon. c. 1870. 15½″ x 20½″

637 Mount Shasta, California. c. 1870. 15½″ x 20½″

Muybridge's most important contribution to photography was his investigation of the movement of animals and human beings, which originated in 1872 with a controversy about the leg movements of a trotting horse. The investigation originally undertaken for Leland Stanford at Palo Alto was greatly extended under the auspices of the University of Pennsylvania in 1883-85. The following plates which are taken from the monumental publication *Animal Locomotion* (1887), were taken with 12-36 separate cameras, and showed for the first time movements too fast for the eye to perceive. Muybridge's photographs not only exposed the absurdity of the conventional "rocking-horse" attitude illustrated by painters of horses, but by projecting them with his zoopraxiscope in rapid movement upon a screen, he paved the way for cinematography.

638 Race horse. 1884-85. Collotype. 12″ x 9″

639 Greyhound. 1884-85. Collotype. 17¾″ x 6¾″

640 Bucking mule. 1884-85. Collotype. 12¼″ x 9¾″

641 Vulture. 1884-85. Collotype. 10½″ x 10½″

642 Fencers. 1884-85. Collotype. 16″ x 6¾″

643 High jump. 1884-85. Collotype. 18″ x 6″

644 Girl throwing a ball. 1884-85. Collotype. 14″ x 8¼″

645 Girl dancing. 1884-85. Collotype. 16¼″ x 6¾″

Nadar, 1820-1910
(Pseudonym for Gaspard Félix Tournachon)

French balloonist, caricaturist, author and photographer. From the mid-fifties on Nadar's studio in the Boulevard des Capucines was a meeting place for the intelligentsia of Paris. Here was held the first exhibition of the Impressionists in April-May, 1874. The trained eye of the caricaturist, accustomed to grasping quickly the characteristic features of the sitter, led to expressive photographic portraits which in their simplicity and natural pose stand in pleasant contrast to the majority of professional portraits of that time. Nadar took the first photograph from a balloon (1858)— and a more successful series in 1862—a feat immortalized by Daumier's lithograph (No. 839). A couple of years later Nadar made the first underground photographs of the catacombs and sewers of Paris by electric light from a Bunsen battery.

646 Christine Roux, the original Musette of Henri Murger's *La Vie de Boheme*. c. 1856. Probably taken as a study for Ingres' "La Source." (rep.)

647 "George Sand." 1864. Carbon print. 7½″ x 9½″

648 Ernest Legouvé. c. 1868. Carbon print. 7½″ x 9½″

649 Baron J. Taylor. c. 1865. Carbon print. 7½″ x 9½″

650 Violet-Le-Duc. c. 1878. Carbon print. 7½″ x 9½″

651 Louis Figuier. c. 1875. Carbon print. 7½″ x 9½″

652 Emile Augier. c. 1865. Carbon print. 7½″ x 9½″

653 Victor Hugo on his deathbed. 22 May, 1885. Woodburytype. 5½″ x 4″

Paul Nadar, 1856-1939
(Son of Felix Tournachon)

Before retiring from photography and leaving the studio under the management of his son, Nadar *père* pioneered a new field—photo-journalism. He interviewed the scientist M. E. Chevreul on the eve of his hundredth birthday and put to him a number of questions which a stenographer wrote down, together with Chevreul's answers, while Paul Nadar took a series of photographs. Thirteen of them were published with questions and answers in *Le journal illustré* on 5 September, 1886.

654 The first photo-interview. M. E. Chevreul answering Nadar's questions. August, 1886. Enl. rep.

Frau E. Nothmann

Amateur photographer in Berlin at the turn of the century.

655 "In the Garden." c. 1897. Photogravure of a gum print. (rep.)

George Oddner, b. 1923

Swedish fashion and advertising photographer active in Malmö. Originally a jazz musician, Oddner was trained after World War II in typography and layout by a Swedish advertising agency, which persuaded him to take up photography and opened a studio for him in Malmö in 1950. In addition to industrial and commercial photography Oddner does fashion and reportage work for leading Swedish magazines. The photographs exhibited were taken on one of several journeys for the Scandinavian airline SAS. Member of the Swedish photographers' association "Tio."

656 Blind beggar in Peru. 1955. 15½″ x 11¾″

657 Mother Earth. Peru. 1955. 11¾″ x 15½″

658 Man with load. Peru. 1955. 15⅜″ x 11⅜″

659 Child selling potatoes. Peru. 1955. 15⅜″ x 11¾″

Timothy H. O'Sullivan, c. 1840-1882

Assistant of Alexander Gardner in Brady's Washington portrait studio before the Civil War, during which he worked for Gardner. Nearly half the photographs in Gardner's *Photographic Sketchbook of the War* (No. 859) are by O'Sullivan. From 1867-69 he took part in government surveys along the 40th Parallel, and later in the Isthmus of Panama and on other explorations.

660 "Harvest of Death." After the Battle of Gettysburg. July, 1863. 10″ x 8¼″

661 Castle Murray near Auburn, Virginia, 1863. 9⅛″ x 7″

Antonio Perini

Architectural photographer in Venice.

662 Entrance to the Doge's Palace, Venice, c. 1860. 10″ x 13″

663 Palazzo Contarini-Fasan, Venice. c. 1860. 12½″ x 10¼″

Carlo Ponti

Leading Venetian architectural photographer specializing in views of Venice, Padua, and Verona. Published in the 1860's a number of albums under the title *Ricordo di Venezia,* each containing 20 large views, some by other Venetian photographers such as Perini. Ponti also made an interesting documentation of Venetian street traders in the early 1860's.

664 A canal in Venice. c. 1865. 13¼″ x 10½″

665 Piazza di S. Marco, Venice. c. 1860. 10½″ x 13½″

666 Staircase of the Doge's Palace, Venice. c. 1860. 10¼″ x 13¼″

667 Greek bronze horses on the Basilica di S. Marco, Venice. c. 1860. 15″ x 10¼″

668 The Basilica di S. Antonio, Padua. c. 1865. 13¾″ x 10½″

Herbert Ponting, 1871-1935

English landscape photographer and traveler. Official photographer to Captain Scott's second and last South Pole expedition, 1910-12. Author of *The Great White South* and *In Lotus-Land Japan.*

669 The "Terra Nova" in the Antarctic ice.

670 An iceberg grotto.

(Enlargements from original 8″ x 10″ negatives in the collection of Paul Popper.)

William Lake Price, ?-1896

English watercolor artist, changed to photography in 1854. One of the earliest in Britain to compose historical and literary subjects and to make composition pictures from several negatives. He also took portraits of the royal family and artists, and reproduced Old Master paintings and frescoes in Rome. Gave up his photographic career in 1862. Wrote *A Manual of Photographic Manipulation* (1858), the first handbook to stress the aesthetic aspect of photography.

671 Dead game. c. 1855. Enl. rep. from an album of his photographs. Size of original 7¼″ x 9¾″

Man Ray, b. 1890

Born in Philadelphia, Ray was one of the first American abstract painters, and became co-founder with Duchamp and Picabia of the New York Dada group in 1917. Took up photography in 1920 to reproduce his own paintings. Settled in Paris the following year, and in 1922 made abstract photographs called "Rayographs." Published 12 of them under the title *Champs Délicieux* with a preface by Tristan Tzara. Earned a living by reproducing paintings for artists, taking portraits, and advertising photographs. Experimented with various techniques in order to find new means of expression in photography and painting; introduced intentional solarization, 1931. Made a surrealist film *Emak Bakia,* 1926. A collection of Man Ray's photographs entitled *Man Ray* was published in 1934.

672 Portrait of a woman: solarization. 1931. Rep. 12″ x 10″

673 Self-portrait (zincography). 1948. 6½″ x 8″

674 Rayograph. 1958. 9¼″ x 11½″

Oscar Gustave Rejlander, 1813-1875

Swedish portrait painter active in London, c. 1840-1851. After studying art in Rome for a year returned to England and took up photography to make studies for his paintings. Opened a photographic portrait studio in Wolverhampton, 1855; active in London from 1860 until his death. Made studies for artists and anecdotal pictures; was the first in Britain to photograph nudes, 1857. Created a sensation at the Manchester Art Treasures Exhibition, 1857, with his allegorical composition "The Two Ways of Life" printed from over 30 negatives. Rejlander's best photographs are unpretentious *genre* pictures, and lively studies for his and other artists' paintings. Was commissioned by Darwin to make illustrations for *The Expression of the Emotions in Man and Animals* (1872) (see No. 862.)

675 Two sisters. c. 1858. 6″ x 8″

676 Girl at window. c. 1864. 6″ x 8″

677 "Family Likeness." 1866. 9″ x 7¼″

678 Album containing 59 photographs: *genre* pictures, studies for artists, and some of the separate figures for "The Two Ways of Life." Nos. 679-683 are enlarged reproductions from this album; the dimensions are those of the originals.

679 The milkmaid. c. 1857. 6¼″ x 8½″. (rep.)

680 Boys tossing chestnuts. c. 1857. 6¼″ x 8½″. (rep.)

681 "Summer" (Mrs. Rejlander). c. 1857. 6″ x 8″. (rep.)

682 Vase and hands. c. 1860. 7½″ x 6″. (rep.)

683 Nude. c. 1857. 6″ x 8¼″. (rep.)

Albert Renger-Patzsch, b. 1897

German professional photographer from 1922 onward and pioneer of "New Objectivity" in photography. His straightforward close-ups of plants and man-made objects, rendered with brilliant textural quality, and his objective views of nature, were in startling contrast to the artificial style then prevalent in photography. His book *Die Welt ist Schön (The World Is Beautiful)* (1928) showed the beauty of everyday objects and exerted an enormous influence, introducing a new vision in photography. Renger-Patzsch's realistic, objective approach was in direct contrast to the very subjective experimental work at the Bauhaus. For some years he taught at the Folkwang School at Essen. He published a large number of topographical books, and books concerned with natural subjects such as trees, stones, etc. Awarded German cultural prize for photography, 1960.

684 Tropical orchid. 1923. 8″x 10″

685 The potter's hands. 1925. 15″ x 11″

686 Landscape near Essen. 1929. 11″ x 15″

687 Fisherman of the Halligen Islands off Schleswig. 1926. 15″ x 11″

688 Crab-fisherwoman. 1927. 11″ x 15″

689 Breakwater. 1926. 11″ x 15″

690 Agavia. 1924. 11″ x 14½″

691 Merry-go-round. 1928. 10⅜″ x 15″

692 A plant. 1922. 11″ x 15″

693 Carpenter's tools 1928. 14½″ x 10½″

694 Willow trees. 1925. 15″ x 11¼″

(All photographs are enlargements from 9 x 12 cm. negatives)

Jacob A. Riis, 1849-1914

A Danish carpenter, Riis emigrated to America in 1870 and seven years later became a police-court reporter for the *New York Tribune.* In 1887 he began a series of flashlight photographs of New York slums, believing that the camera was a mightier weapon than the pen for attacking the bad social conditions responsible for crime. Thus Riis became America's first photo-reporter. His pictures influenced Theodore Roosevelt, then governor of New York State, to undertake a number of social reforms, including the wiping out of the notorious tenements at Mulberry Bend. Today the Jacob A. Riis Neighborhood Settlement commemorates the photographer's great work. Riis wrote and illustrated, among other books, *How the Other Half Lives* (1890) and *Children of the Poor* (1892).

695 Bandits' roost, Mulberry Street, New York. 1888. 9½" x 11½"

696 Home of an Italian rag-picker, New York. 1888. 11½" x 9½"

697 Tailor's sweatshop, New York. 1888. 11½" x 9½"

698 Night shelter for the homeless, Bayard Street, New York. 1891. 11½" x 9½"

699 Slum dweller in coal-cellar, New York. 1891.

(Nos. 695-698 are enlargements from Riis' negatives in the Museum of the City of New York.)

James Robertson

Scottish medal designer and chief engraver to the Imperial Mint at Constantinople in the 1850's. Robertson was also an excellent photographer of views, working sometimes in collaboration with the Italian photographer A. Beato. In the mid-fifties Robertson published a series of views of Constantinople, Malta, Athens and Jerusalem. Arriving in the Crimea immediately after the fall of Sebastopol in September, 1855, Robertson completed in a way the war reportage of Roger Fenton by taking about 60 photographs of the Russian batteries, the English and French trenches, and the ruins of Sebastopol. In association with Beato, he made a valuable documentation two years later of the scenes of the Indian Mutiny.

700 Malta fortress. c. 1860. Enl. rep. of a 10" x 8" photograph.

701 Interior of the Redan, Sebastopol. September, 1855. 12" x 8½"

702 Interior of the Malakoff Tower, Sebastopol, with the French semaphore station. September, 1855. 11½" x 9"

Henry Peach Robinson, 1830-1901

English professional portrait photographer from 1857 on. Originally wanted to be a painter but became instead a "painter" in photography with his elaborate composition pictures made for exhibitions, which were strictly speaking photomontages made up from prints from several negatives. Robinson was the most influential artist-photographer in the second half of the nineteenth century. In a number of books he laid down the rules for artistic photography: all unfortunately very artificial and derived from painting. Robinson's exhibition pictures look like photographically produced paintings of the Pre-Raphaelites (No. 703) or Josef Israels (Nos. 704, 705). Robinson considered "The Lady of Shalott" "a ghastly mistake," as going "beyond the limits of the life of our day," but he accounted Nos. 704 and 705 among his best compositions. All three photographs are Robinson's own exhibition pictures.

703 "The Lady of Shalott." 1861. 20½" x 12". Combination print from two negatives—landscape, and boat with the model. Influenced by Sir John Millais' painting "Ophelia."

704 "When the Day's Work is Done." 1877. Toned platinotype. 29½" x 21". Combination print from six negatives.

705 "Dawn and Sunset." 1885. Toned platinotype. 29½" x 21". Combination print from five negatives.

Arthur Rothstein, b. 1915

American reportage photographer since 1934, Rothstein made in 1935-36 a series of impressive documentary photographs for the Farm Security Administration. Later on he photographed for the U. S. Army, the United Nations, and in particular the magazine *Look*, of which he is now technical director of photography.

706 Sharecropper's wife. 1935. 10½" x 13½"

707 Sharecropper's wife and child. 1935. 11½″ x 14½″

708 Dust storm, Cimarron County, Oklahoma. 1936. 13¼″ x 11½″

709 Home of Postmaster Brown, Old Rag, Virginia. 1935. 14¼″ x 11¼″

(Enlargements from the original negatives at the Library of Congress)

Harry C. Rubincam

Amateur photographer in Denver, Colorado, before World War I. Member of the Photo-Secession.

710 Circus rider. 1905. Photogravure. 8″ x 6″

Erich Salomon, 1886-1944

Pioneer of political reportage, Dr. Salomon after studying law, worked in the publicity department of the Ullstein publishing firm. Started in February 1928 as a free-lance photo-reporter after the sensational success of his photograph of a murder trial. The Ermanox and later the Leica cameras with their wide aperture lenses, in conjunction with fast negative material, opened up new fields in photography: reportage in interiors by available light. Dissatisfied with the static pictures that appeared in the *Berliner Illustrirte,* Dr. Salomon astonished the world by his candid snapshots of statesmen and others, taken when they were off their guard. Aristide Briand called him "le roi des indiscrets." Published *Berühmte Zeitgenossen in unbewachten Augenblicken (Famous Contemporaries in Unguarded Moments)* (1931). Being Jewish, Dr. Salomon emigrated to Holland in 1934, but was murdered ten years later in Auschwitz extermination camp.

711 Fritjof Nansen interviewed by a British journalist at the League of Nations, Geneva. 1928.

712 Dr. Salomon showing Sir Austen Chamberlain, the British Foreign Secretary, the photographs which he had taken of the Locarno Conference. London, 1929.

713 Marlene Dietrich telephoning from Hollywood to her daughter in Berlin, shortly after the opening of the transatlantic telephone. 1930.

714 The second Hague Conference on Reparations, January, 1930. Among the French and German ministers and financial experts are André Tardieu and Dr. Julius Curtius. Photograph taken at 11 p.m.

715 The same meeting at 2 a.m.

716 Banquet at the Quai d'Orsay, Paris, 1931. Aristide Briand (left), Heinrich Bruening, Julius Curtius, Edouard Herriot (right). No photographers were admitted, but Briand had made a bet that Salomon would somehow manage to get in. When he actually appeared, Briand called out in triumph: "Ah, le voilà, le roi des indiscrets!"

717 Mussolini, Bruening, Curtius and Grandi at a discussion in the Hotel Excelsior, Rome. August, 1931.

718 Edouard Benes, Lord Samuel and Lord Simon during the Disarmament Conference at Geneva. 1932.

(All photographs are approx. 16″ x 12″ enlargements from the original 1¾″ x 2¼″ negatives in the possession of Peter Hunter, Dr. Salomon's surviving eldest son.)

Lyddell Sawyer, b. 1856

English professional portrait and landscape photographer, first in Newcastle, and from 1895 onward in London.

719 In the Castle Garth, Newcastle. 1888. 5½″ x 7¼″. Photogravure.

720 In the Twilight. 1888. 7¼″ x 5½″. Photogravure.

721 Waiting for the Boats. 1889. 7¼″ x 5½″. Photogravure.

Christian Schad, b. 1894

German painter, founder member of the Zürich Dada group in 1917. The following year he made abstract photograms which Tristan Tzara called "Schadographs" and showed later on to Man Ray who proceeded to make "Rayographs." From 1918-25 Schad worked in Rome, and adopted the New Realism style in painting. From 1928-42 he was active in Berlin.

722 & 723 Two Schadographs made with strips of paper, string etc. laid on light-sensitive paper and exposed under an electric lamp. Replicas of lost pictures specially made for the Gernsheim Collection in 1960. Each 7" x 9½".

Prof. Schardin

Director of Scientific Research Institute at Weil am Rhein, Germany.

724 Temperature spread around a heated metal tube. 1951. 9½" x 7"

725 Air-waves caused by a bullet flying through the smoke of two lighted candles. 1951. 7" x 9½"

Toni Schneiders, b. 1920

German professional photographer. Worked first for the French Army of occupation, and since 1950 as a free-lance architectural and industrial photographer.

726 Onion flowers. 1948. 14¾" x 11½"

727 Railway signals. 1950. 11½" x 17¾"

728 Ice formation. 1953. 12" x 15¼"

729 Window reflections. 1953. 9¾" x 16½"

C. Schwartz

Professional portrait photographer in Berlin.

730 Christian Rauch, sculptor. 1852. 6" x 8"

Shearn & Sons

Firm of professional photographers in Cambridge, England.

731 Undergraduates' demonstration against the admission of women to full membership of the University of Cambridge. June, 1897. Enl. rep. of 8½" x 6½" photograph.

Samuel Shere, b. 1905

American press photographer working for International News Photos in New York. Shere's unforgettable photograph of the "Hindenburg" explosion will always remain one of the most impressive news pictures.

732 Explosion of the zeppelin "Hindenburg" on arrival at Lakehurst, New Jersey. May, 1937. Enlargement from original negative by courtesy of International News Photos.

Camille Silvy

A French diplomat, Silvy gave up his career in 1859 to become a professional portrait photographer, having been an amateur the last few years. He introduced the carte-de-visite format into England at his studio in London and soon became the most fashionable portrait photographer of high society and was known as "the Winterhalter of photography." In 1869 when the fashion for carte portraits was beginning to wane, Silvy sold his business. After the Franco-Prussian War he started a studio in a fashionable suburb of Paris.

733 Call-up notice to the army for Napoleon III's Italian campaign against Austria. May, 1859. Enl. rep.

A. G. Dew Smith

Lens-grinder at Cambridge University Observatory, England, and amateur photographer in the 1880's and '90's. A friend of Robert Louis Stevenson and many other literary figures; immortalized as Atwater in *The Ebb Tide* by R. L. Stevenson.

734 Robert Louis Stevenson. 1885. Toned platinotype. 10¾" x 13¾"

735 W. E. Henley with his bust by Rodin. 1887. 14½" x 11¾"

736 G. E. Fitzgerald. 1891. 11½" x 14½"

737 Prof. Theodor Mommsen. c. 1895. Photogravure. 8" x 10"

738 Joseph Joachim. c. 1890. Photogravure. 11¾" x 15½"

739 Prof. Fleeming Jenkin. 1885. Platinotype. 11¾" x 15"

C. Srna

A Viennese photographer.

740 Hamburg harbor. 1886. Enl. rep. of original 6½" x 4¾" photograph.

Edward J. Steichen, b. 1879

Born in Luxembourg, educated in Milwaukee, Steichen has been a photographer since 1896 and was director of the photographic department of the Museum of Modern Art, New York, 1947-62. Founder-member of the Photo-Secession 1902, Steichen was a prominent exhibitor of impressionistic photographs before World War I, during which he was chief of aerial photography in the American expeditionary forces. After the war Steichen destroyed his "arty" gum prints and started straight photography. Chief photographer of *Vogue* and *Vanity Fair* 1923-37, taking fashion photographs and portraits of leading personalities. During World War II was in command of U. S. Navy combat photography. In collaboration with Wayne Miller arranged the famous "Family of Man" exhibition, 1955.

741 Paul Robeson as "The Emperor Jones." 1933. 6½″ x 8¼″

Otto Steinert, b. 1915

Born at Saarbrücken, doctor med. Berlin, 1939. Gave up medicine in 1948 and became teacher of photography at, and later director of, the State School of Applied Art at Saarbrücken. Since 1959 Prof. Steinert has been head of the photographic department at the Folkwang School, Essen. Founder of "Subjective Photography," 1950; organized three large exhibitions under this title, which also formed the basis of two volumes with the same title, 1952 and 1955. Also published a selection of Hugo Erfurth's portraits, 1961.

742 Call-up notice, Paris. 1950. 11½″ x 16″

743 Landscape in the Saar district. 1953. 11¾″ x 15¾″

744 Snow tracks (negative montage). 1954. 15¾″ x 11¾″

745 Interchangeable forms (negative montage) 1955. 15¾″ x 11¾″

Alfred Stieglitz, 1864-1946

Born at Hoboken, educated in New York and at the Berlin Polytechnic, returned to New York in 1890 and worked for five years at a photoengraving firm. In 1892 Stieglitz began taking street-life photographs in New York with a hand camera. After retiring from business, he devoted himself for the rest of his life to furthering creative photography and, later, the recognition of modern art. An advocate of straight photography,

Stieglitz founded the Photo-Secession, 1902, and edited *Camera Work,* 1903-17. At Steichen's suggestion, opened and directed Photo-Secession gallery at 291 Fifth Avenue, 1905-17, where he introduced the work of modern photographers and many *avant-garde* artists. Director of "Intimate Gallery," 1925, and "An American Place," 1929-46.

746 Winter—Fifth Avenue. 1892. Photogravure. 6″ x 8″

747 The Terminal. 1893. Photogravure. 8⅛″ x 6″

748 Spring showers, New York. 1900. Photogravure. 4″ x 8″

749 New York Central Station. 1903. Photogravure. 8″ x 6″

750 Going to the Post. 1904. Photogravure. 6″ x 7¼″

751 The Steerage. 1907. Photogravure. 6″ x 8″

752 City of Ambition. 1910. Photogravure. 8″ x 6″

753 Nude (in collaboration with Clarence H. White). c. 1910. Photogravure. 6″ x 8″

Sir Benjamin Stone, 1838-1914

Member of Parliament for Birmingham, England, and founder of the National Photographic Record Association, 1897. The members of this society photographed ancient customs and traditional ceremonies that were dying out. Stone, himself, was the most active member of the Association. He was the first person permitted to photograph a Coronation (George V's, 1911) inside Westminster Abbey. Published a selection of his photographs in a two-volume work: *Sir Benjamin Stone's Pictures,* 1905.

754 Roasting an ox at Stratford-on-Avon fair. c. 1898. Rep.

Paul Strand, b. 1890

American photographer and cinematographer, living near Paris since 1948. Learned photography from Lewis Hine in 1907, and five years later set up as a commercial photographer. Strand's street-life photographs of New York, 1915, advocating a new realism in photography, were far in advance of the artistic photography of his time. Free-lance news-reel photographer 1922-32, and from 1933-34 chief photographer and cinematographer to the Mexican Ministry of Education. From 1926 onward Strand made close-up still photographs of natural forms, similar to though quite independent from the New Objectivity of Renger-Patzsch. Published a number of books illustrated with photographs taken in Mexico, New England, France, Italy, the Hebrides. Paul Strand's photographs of 1915-16 — the last to be published by Stieglitz in *Camera Work* — are particularly significant because they broke new ground in several fields: New Objectivity, reportage, abstract patterns.

755 Bowls. 1915. Photogravure. 6½″ x 9″

756 New York. 1915. Photogravure. 6½″ x 9¼″

757 Man with bowler hat, New York. 1915. Photogravure. 6½″ x 9″

758 Blind woman, New York. 1915. Photogravure. 6″ x 8¾″

759 Old woman, New York. 1915. Photogravure. 6½″ x 9″

760 Shadows and forms. 1916. Photogravure. 9½″ x 6½″

761 The white fence. 1916. Photogravure. 8″ x 6¼″

762 Statue of Christ at Huexotla, Mexico. 1933. Photogravure. 8″ x 10″

763 Statue of the Madonna in the Church of San Felipe, Oaxa, Mexico, 1933. Photogravure. 8″ x 10″

764 Gateway in Hidalgo, Mexico. 1933. Photogravure. 8″ x 10″

765 Boy in Uruapan, Mexico. 1933. Photogravure. 8″ x 10″

Karl F. Strauss

A New York member of the Photo-Secession.

766 Over the roof-tops, Meissen, Germany. c. 1908. Photogravure. 5″ x 9″

Wolfgang Suschitzky, b. 1912

Viennese by birth, Suschitzky studied photography in Vienna 1930-33, and has been domiciled in London since 1936. Before World War II he specialized largely in photographs of children and animals. Since the war he has been working on documentary films.

767 Gorilla. 1938. 9¼″ x 11¼″

768 Two camels. 1938. 9¼″ x 11¼″

769 Road repair workers. 1939. 10″ x 12″

770 Little girl. 1939. 9″ x 11¼″

(All photographs are enlargements from 2¼″ x 2¼″ negatives.)

John Thomson, 1837-1921

Scottish explorer and photographer. Thomson had already published important ethnographical works illustrated with his photographs taken during ten years' travels in China, Siam, and Cambodia, when he undertook the first photo-documentation of London street life in 1876. This series is the first social documentation by photography. The living conditions of the London poor were described partly by Thomson and partly by a journalist, Adolphe Smith, and published with Thomson's photographs as *Street Life in London,* 1877. (See No. 866.) In 1880 Thomson pioneered another field — "at home" portraiture of celebrities.

771 Italian street musicians. 1876.

772 Outside the pub. 1876.

773 Old woman with baby. 1876.

774 Street photographer. 1876.

775 Shoeshine. 1876.

776 Old clothes shop. 1876.

777 Italian ice-cream seller. 1876.

778 Recruiting sergeants. 1876.

(All photographs are enlarged reproductions from Thomson's book *Street Life in London,* see No. 866. The original size of the photographs is approx. 3½″ x 4¾″.)

Sir Emery Walker, 1851-1933

Process-engraver and printer in London. Collaborator and friend of William Morris, whom he helped to establish the Kelmscott Press. Amateur photographer.

779 William Morris. January 1889. Photogravure. 8½" x 10¾"

William Warnecke

Press photgrapher on the staff of the *New York World Telegram*.

780 Assassination of Mayor William J. Gaynor of New York. 1910. Enlargement from original 4" x 6" negative in the possession of the *New York World-Telegram*.

Herbert Watkins

London portrait photographer between c. 1855 - c. 1875.

781 Charles Dickens. 1859. Enl. rep. from Lewis Carroll's album of collected photographs. Original size 6" x 8".

Brett Weston, b. 1911

Second son of Edward Weston, who taught him photography. Had a portrait studio in Mexico 1925-1928; afterwards assisted his father in various portrait studios in California. When his father became ill, Brett Weston took over all photographic activities. Awarded Guggenheim Fellowship 1947. Edward Weston's training comes out clearly in his son's style. He is interested in the same subjects, which he photographs with equal objectivity, and nearly always makes contact prints from his 8" x 10" negatives.

782 Window, New York. 1945. 9¾" x 7¾"

783 Desert plant, California. 1946. 9½" x 7½"

784 Marsh plant, North Carolina. 9½" x 7½"

785 Sand dunes. 1950. 9½" x 7½"

Edward Weston, 1886-1958

Began his career as an ordinary itinerant photographer in California; opened a portrait studio in 1911, and also made conventional "Salon" pictures for exhibitions. During a three-year stay in Mexico City as portrait photographer 1923-6 Weston came under the influence of Diego Rivera and changed his style completely. After return-ing to California in 1927 Weston started making sharp objective photographs and close-ups of unusual natural forms. Opened portrait studio with his son Brett, first in San Francisco, later at Carmel. Founder member of the F.64 Group, 1932. A Guggenheim Fellowship in 1937 enabled Weston to devote himself exclusively to landscapes and close-ups of nature, selections of which were published in his books *California and the West* (1940) and *My Camera on Point Lobos* (1950). He worked almost exclusively with 8" x 10" negatives and rarely made enlargements.

786 Paprica. 1930. 8" x 10"

787 Eroded rock, Point Lobos. 1934. 8" x 10"

788 Sand dunes, Oceano. 1936. 10" x 8"

789 Guadalupe de Rivera, Mexico. 1924. Enlargement from 4" x 5" negative.

790 Wrecked auto on the beach. 1937. 10" x 8"

Clarence H. White, 1871-1925

For sixteen years head bookkeeper in a wholesale grocery firm at Newark, Ohio, and amateur photographer from 1894 onward. Founder member of the Photo-Secession 1902, White was an advocate of straight photography. Lecturer on photography at Columbia University, New York, from 1907 until his death, and at his own summer school of photography from 1910-25. Also instructor at the Brooklyn Institute of Arts and Sciences from 1908-21.

791 Lady in black. 1898. Photogravure. 6" x 8"

(See also No. 753.)

Henry White, 1819-1903

Partner in a firm of London solicitors, and prominent amateur photographer from 1854-c. 1864. One of the earliest artistic landscape photographers and considered by many of his contemporaries the best.

792 A cornfield. August 1856. 9¾" x 7¾"

793 Bramble and ivy. c. 1856. 9" x 11"

Benjamin Gay Wilkinson, 1857-1927

London solicitor from 1881-1926, and keen amateur photographer and exhibitor from 1877 onward. Follower of the Naturalistic school of photography, and founder member of the Linked Ring 1892.

794 Sand Dunes. Photogravure. 1889. 7" x 5"

Charles A. Wilson, 1865-1958

Scottish photographer of views, son of George Washington Wilson. After their father's death in 1893 Charles Wilson and his brothers continued the family business in Aberdeen until 1908. His views of London in the 1880's were taken unobserved from a hired removal van with a hole cut in front for the lens.

795 Oxford Circus, London. c. 1887.

796 Piccadilly, London. c. 1887.

797 Clapham Road, London. c. 1887.

798 Ludgate Circus, London. c. 1887.

799 Fleet Street, London. c. 1887.

800 Oxford Street, London. c. 1887.

(All photographs are contact copies from the original 10" x 12" negatives.)

George Washington Wilson, 1823-1893

Professional portrait and landscape photographer in Aberdeen from 1853 onward. Wilson was among the earliest to take instantaneous street views with traffic. He was appointed photographer to Queen Victoria in Scotland c. 1860. Built up an extensive business in publishing photographs of all countries, which was second in size only to the firm of Francis Frith. G. W. Wilson & Co. was also the largest producer of lantern slide pictures.

801 Princes Street, Edinburgh. 1859. Enl. rep. from a stereoscopic photograph.

Rolf Winquist, b. 1910

Swedish professional photographer, born in Gothenburg and active in Stockholm in the fields of portraiture, fashion, and advertising. Member of the Swedish photographers' association "Tio."

802 Photogram. 1952. 9" x 11½"

803 The Swedish actress Gertrud Fridh as Medea. 1951. 13¾" x 18"

804 The Swedish actress Marianne Hermannsson. 1953. 15¼" x 19"

805 The Swedish actress Margit Carlquist. 1955. 13¾" x 16¼"

Wood and Gibson

American photographers who took pictures of the Civil War for Alexander Gardner.

806 Ruins of Norfolk naval arsenal, Virginia. April, 1861. 10" x 8¼"

807 Troop inspection at Cumberland Landing, Virginia. 1862. 10" x 8¼"

808 Battery near Yorktown, Virginia. 1862. 9⅛" x 6¾"

Anonymous American Photographers

809 Italian emigrant children selling fruit at Mulberry Bend, New York. 1895. Enl. rep.

810 Two poor New York children with loaves of bread. 1895. Enl. rep.

811 President Theodore Roosevelt making his inaugural address outside the Capitol, Washington. 5 March 1905. Enl. rep. from a stereoscopic photograph.

Anonymous English Photographers

812 Deerstalking at Achnacarry, Scotland. Lord Malmesbury and keepers. 1859. 10" x 8"

813 Election of parliamentary candidates at Dover. 1863. Enl. rep. from 4¼" x 6½" photograph.

814 Mrs. William Morris posed by D. G. Rossetti. July 1865. 10" x 12"

815 Chinese pirates shortly before their execution at Kowloon, Hongkong. May 1891. 10½" x 8¼"

816 The same, immediately after beheading. 10½" x 8¼"

Anonymous French Photographers

817-823 Seven photographs of the Franco-Prussian War 1870-71.

824-829 Six photographs of the Paris Commune 1871.

830 Paris World Exhibition, 1889. Under the Eiffel Tower. Enl. rep. from a photograph. 7¼″ x 4¾″

Anonymous Italian Photograper

Two photographs of victims of the Vesuvius eruption in A.D. 79. Photographed at Pompeii in 1865.

831 Mother and daughter. 9½″ x 8″

832 A slave. 9½″ x 8″

Anonymous Swiss Photographer

833-835 Three photo-elasticity pictures showing stress patterns in sheets of synthetic material under pressure. All 9½″ x 11¾″ enl. from 3½″ x 4¾″ negatives at the Federal Institute for Testing Materials, Zürich.

Photomontages

836-838 Three photomontages from the album of Sir Edward Blount, financier and railway magnate. c. 1873. Photomontages were not the invention of John Heartfield and George Grosz, as frequently assumed, but were often made by nineteenth-century amateurs, and some professional photographers like H. P. Robinson. The surrealistic effect of these montages is astonishing, and only goes to prove that there are early prototypes for everything. The watercolor painting is sometimes by Sir Edward Blount, and sometimes by other members of his family, or friends.

Lithographs

(See also Nos. 145-148)

839 **Honoré Daumier,** "Nadar Elevant la Photographie à l'Hauteur de l'Art." Proof print. 8¼″ x 10½″. Published in *Le boulevard* 25 May 1862.

840 **Henri de Toulouse-Lautrec.** "Paul Sescau — Photographe." 4-color lithograph made in 1894 for his photographer friend, whose studio was at 9 Place Pigalle, Paris. (Reduced facsimile.)

841 **Henri de Toulouse-Lautrec.** "Nib, ou le Photographe Amateur." Lithograph made in January 1895 and published as a supplement to *La revue blanche.*

NINETEENTH-CENTURY PHOTOGRAPHICALLY ILLUSTRATED BOOKS AND JOURNALS

(A small selection from the 365 titles in the Gernsheim Collection.)

The earliest books with illustrations based on photography were published in Paris in the early 1840's. They had lithographs or engravings copied from daguerreotypes, and the intervention of the artist makes it difficult to ascertain to what extent the original may have been altered by him, apart from the usual "improvement" of adding figures, carriages, etc., to enliven the view.

In contrast to Daguerre's silvered copper plates, photographs on paper could be used direct for book illustration without the necessity for an artist to copy them. Talbot patented in 1841 the idea of photographic publication, and was the first, and until 1851 the only person, to publish photographically illustrated books. *The Pencil of Nature* (1844-46) (No. 78) and *Sun Pictures in Scotland* (1845) (No. 80) appear to have been published in very small editions, for barely a dozen complete copies of each have so far been traced. To popularize the Calotype Talbot published an article in *The Art Journal,* London, June 1846 (No. 846) illustrated with one original Calotype. This magazine had 7,000 subscribers, and the "sun printing" and mounting of the large number of photographs of a great variety of subjects was carried out at Talbot's printing establishment at Reading, Berkshire.

Some of the illustrated books were an astonishing feat in production. Henry Taunt's guidebook (No. 864), for example, is illustrated with no fewer than 80 small photographs, all pasted in by hand in the correct order and on the right page.

England was leading in this type of book. Between 1844 and 1875 about 450 were published, mostly in luxury editions. The number of photographically illustrated books that appeared in France, Germany, Italy and the U.S.A. is very much smaller. So far, no specialized bibliographies have been published, but it is doubtful whether the rest of the world produced as many as 450 such books altogether. Today, some of these *incunabula* of photographic book publishing are great rarities. The editions were never very large, in one case (No. 848) amounting to only twelve copies!

After about 1875 the photographs in illustrated books were usually produced by one of the "permanent" printing processes such as carbon and Woodburytype (see No. 866) or by photo-mechanical printing processes such as the heliotype (see No. 862). Only after the introduction of the half-tone block was it possible to print photographs together with the text, and from 1883 onward one finds such illustrations now and then in books and magazines. The general introduction began, however, only in the twentieth century.

The number of photographically illustrated newspapers and magazines is very small indeed. Until about 1900 they relied on wood-engravings, occasionally copied from photographs. In January 1904 *The Daily Mirror* in London became the first newspaper in the world to abandon wood-engraving and to be illustrated exclusively with photographs in half-tone.

842   Charles Philipon, ed. *Paris et ses environs, réproduits par le Daguerréotype.* Paris, 1840. Contains 60 lithographs copied from daguerreotypes.

843   N. P. Lerebours, ed. *Excursions daguerriennes.* Paris. Vol. II. 1843. Besides 49 copperplate engravings copied from daguerreotypes, this volume also contains two photo-etchings made direct from etched daguerreotypes by Hippolyte Fizeau's process.

844   W. H. Fox Talbot. *The Pencil of Nature.* Part I. London 1844. (See No. 78.)

845   W. H. Fox Talbot. *Sun Pictures in Scotland.* London 1845. (See No. 80.)

846 *The Art Journal: Monthly Journal of the Arts.* London. June 1846. Illustrated with one Calotype, in many cases taken by Talbot himself. Each of the many copies of this journal that we have seen has a different illustration; most are rather badly faded. The first magazine illustrated with a photograph.

847   Maxime Du Camp. *Egypte, Nubie, Palestine et Syrie.* Paris and London. 1852. (See No. 152.)

848   Sir William Stirling. *The Cloister Life of the Emperor Charles the Fifth.* London. 1853. According to a printed notice, only 12 copies of this book were illustrated with photographs (18 in number).

849   Horace. *Quinti Horatii Flacci Opera.* Paris. 1855. Illustrated with 18 photographs. There is also another edition of the same publication with only six photographs.

850   M. Digby Wyatt. *Notices of Sculpture in Ivory.* London. 1856. Contains nine photographs by J. A. Spencer. The first art-historical work illustrated with photographs.

851   C. Piazzi Smyth. *Teneriffe: an Astronomer's Experiment.* London. 1858. Illustrated with 20 stereoscopic photographs by the author. The first of several books illustrated with stereoscopic photographs, having appeared in January. The photographs were looked at through a book stereoscope (see No. 933).

852 *The Stereoscopic Magazine, a Gallery of Landscape, Scenery, Architecture, Antiquities, and Natural History, accompanied with descriptive articles by writers of eminence.* Issued in monthly parts, each illustrated with three stereoscopic photographs. Exhibited is the first number published on 1 July 1858. The only periodical illustrated in this way.

853   Friedrich von Schiller. *Schiller's Gedichte.* Jubilee edition of Schiller's poems. Stuttgart. 1859. Exhibited is the first part containing three photographs. Believed to be the first German publication illustrated with photographs.

854 H. W. Longfellow. *Illustrations of Longfellow's Courtship of Miles Standish.* New York. 1859. Illustrated with 8 photographs by Mathew Brady of drawings by John W. Ehninger. One of the earliest American books illustrated with photographs.

855 Nathaniel Hawthorne. *Transformation, or the Romance of Monte Beni.* Tauchnitz edition, Leipzig. 1860. Contains 53 photographs.

856 *Sunshine in the Country: a Book of Rural Poetry.* London. 1861. Contains 20 photographs by W. M. Grundy.

857 G. B. Duchenne. *Mécanisme de la physionomie humaine.* Paris. 1862. Contains 71 photographs of facial expressions. The first scientific work of this kind.

858 Sir Walter Scott. *The Lady of the Lake.* London. 1863. Contains 14 photographs by Thomas Ogle and G. W. Wilson.

859 Alexander Gardner. *Gardner's Photographic Sketch-book of the War.* Vol. I. Washington. 1865. Illustrated with 50 photographs by Alexander Gardner, T. H. O'Sullivan and other photographers. Only five copies are known to exist.

860 W. B. George. *The Oberland and its Glaciers Explored and Illustrated with Ice-axe and Camera.* London. 1866. Contains 28 photographs by Ernest Edwards.

861 H. B. Small. *The Canadian Handbook and Tourist's Guide, giving a Description of Canadian Lake and River Scenery and Places of Historical Interest.* Ed. by J. Taylor. Montreal. 1866. Contains five photographs from nature by William Notman and five reproductions of paintings (three of them by Kreighoff). Probably the earliest guide-book illustrated with photographs.

862 Charles Darwin. *The Expression of the Emotions in Man and Animals.* London. 1872. Contains 20 heliotypes from photographs by Rejlander, in some of which he and his wife act the required emotions.

863 F. F. Maury and L. A. Duhring. *Photographic Review of Medicine and Surgery: a bi-monthly illustration of interesting cases, accompanied by notes edited by Dr. F. F. Maury and Dr. L. A. Duhring.* Vol. II. Philadelphia. 1872. 24 photographs. This is the earliest medical journal illustrated with photographs.

864 Henry W. Taunt. *A New Map of the River Thames from Oxford to London.* Oxford. 1873. Contains 80 photographs by the author.

865 *The Far East: a monthly journal illustrated with photographs.* Published simultaneously in Tokyo, Shanghai, and Hong Kong. No. 1, Vol I, July, 1876, is exhibited. Each issue contains several photographs—portraits of personalities in the Far East and landscapes.

866 "J T." (John Thomson) and "A. S." (Adolphe Smith). *Street Life in London.* London. 1877. Illustrated with 37 Woodburytypes by John Thomson. (See Nos. 771-778)

867 P. H. Emerson and G. F. Goodall. *Life and Landscape of the Norfolk Broads.* London. 1886. Limited edition of 100 copies. Illustrated with 40 platinotypes by Emerson. (see Nos. 442-446)

868 Armand Silvestre. *Arlette.* Paris. c. 1902. With 100 photographs by E. Lagrange. One of the earliest novels for which characters and events were specially posed and photographed, and reproduced by letterpress.

869 Cuthbert Bede (pseudonym of the Rev. Edward Bradley). *Photographic Pleasures popularly portrayed by Pen and Pencil.* London. 1855. The first book caricaturing photography.

870 Voigtländer daguerreotype camera. January, 1841. Made of brass. The camera, which takes circular pictures 3½″ diameter, has the first mathematically calculated portrait lens, by Joseph Petzval, F 3.6, f 6″. The Petzval lens, which was sixteen times faster than the Chevalier and Lerebours lenses designed for the official daguerreotype outfit, remained the standard lens design for portraiture for several decades. The camera shown is a replica of the original model, and was presented to the Gernsheim Collection by Voigtländer A. G. of Braunschweig, Germany, on the occasion of their bicentenary in 1958.

871 Daguerreotype outfit by Chevallier*, Place de la Bourse, Paris. c. 1845. Made of wood. For quarter-plates 3¼″ x 4¼″. A hinged double door shades the ground-glass for clearer definition when focusing. With the camera is a plate box containing two unexposed silvered copper plates, and the mercury box for developing. The original daguerreotype apparatus was for 6½″ x 8½″ plates, suitable for views and architecture but not portraits because of the length of exposure required. To obtain reasonably short exposures for portraiture ¼-plate and even ⅛-plate apparatus was necessary in the early years.

(*N.B. This optician should not be confused with Charles Chevalier of Place du Pont Neuf)

From c. 1850 for the next four decades cameras were, with few exceptions, cumbersome wooden apparatus with bellows extension, similar to No. 874, only much larger, frequently for plates 10″ x 12″ and even up to 18″ x 24″. Even after enlarging had become practicable through the introduction of fast bromide paper in the 'eighties, most photographers continued making contact copies, and for this reason used large negative sizes. The equipment for a day's outing during the collodion period not infrequently weighed 100 to 120 lbs. or more, for in addition to the camera, a dark-tent, chemicals, dishes, and even water, had to be taken along. To serious photographers

using large plates, the Dubroni camera (No. 873) and a few other small cameras for amateurs, must have seemed ridiculous miniatures—which in a way they were.

872 Sutton's panoramic camera. Patented by Thomas Sutton of Jersey on 29 September, 1859. Special curved glass plates 10″ x 5″ had to be used with the camera, which is made of mahogany. They were carried in a separate plate box which still contains eight glass plates and one exposed collodion negative of an English cathedral. Originally the camera was probably fitted with Sutton's fluid lens, 1859, which had an angle of view of 100°. This lens, which held ½ pint of water, requiring to be changed every day, was not much favored, and in this apparatus has been replaced by an ordinary achromatic landscape lens.

873 Dubroni hand camera. Designed by a French engineer, Dubroni, in 1864, for amateur photographers. In order to dispense with the need for a dark-tent, all the chemical manipulations for the wet collodion process were carried out in an orange glass globe *inside* the camera. The liquids were squeezed into this globe and siphoned off again with a pipette. A peephole at the back of the camera covered with an orange glass (missing) enabled the operator to watch the progress of development. The wooden-box camera was made in five sizes of which this is the smallest, for plates 2″ square. The Dubroni is one of the smallest cameras of the early period.

873 (a) Instruction leaflet for Dubroni's camera.

874 "Universal" plate camera for portraits and landscapes, ordinary and stereoscopic views. Made in London c. 1890. The camera is made of mahogany, has square bellows, double extension, and takes plates 4¼″ x 6½″. Special features are adjustable lens panel, swivel focusing screen, and metal struts to steady the camera body. A Lancaster "Rectigraph" lens is provided for taking ordinary photographs, and a pair of Voigtländer "Euryscope" lenses with a separate lens panel for stereoscopic pictures. Three double slides.

875 "Instantanograph" camera. 1894. Manufactured by J. Lancaster of Birmingham. For quarter-plates. The mahogany camera has conical bellows, double extension, and a Lancaster anastigmat lens. A special feature patented by Lancaster is the insertion of the plate holder without having to remove the ground-glass. Being square, horizontal or vertical pictures could be taken without turning the camera.

876 Thornton-Pickard "Ruby" landscape camera. c. 1895. For 5⅛″ x 7⅛″ plates. Made of mahogany, with triple extension. Zeiss "Protar" wide-angle lens for architectural work, F 18, f 5½″, fitted with a Thornton-Pickard roller-blind shutter. Three double slides, and wooden tripod.

877 Stand camera of French manufacture for 5⅛″ x 7⅛″ plates. c. 1895. Made of mahogany, with double bellows extension. The symmetric anastigmat by H. Duplouich of Paris F 7, f 7⅛″ is fitted with a Thornton-Pickard roller-blind shutter. Three double slides.

878 "Challenge" hand and stand camera made by J. Lizars of Glasgow. 1902. For quarter-plates. Made of mahogany, with double bellows extension, adjustable lens movement, "Brilliant" viewfinder if used as a hand camera, and ground-glass with focusing hood if used as a stand camera. "Challenge" Rapid Rectilinear lens with Bausch & Lomb pneumatic shutter. 1-1/100 second. Three double slides.

Magazine Hand Cameras

After the general introduction of factory-produced gelatine dry plates c. 1880, tens of thousands of amateurs took up photography as a hobby, and chiefly for their benefit hand cameras were put on the market for use with either plates, sheet film, or—from 1889 onward—celluloid rollfilm. In order to make these cameras easy to use, the negative material was usually stored in a magazine inside the camera or attached to it.

879 "Eureka" camera patented 5 May, 1887, by W. W. Rouch, London. In outward appearance it resembles the first Kodak (see No. 887), though made of mahogany and slightly larger. Fitted with a double anastigmat with iris diaphragm F 6 and a roller-blind shutter behind the lens giving between 1/15 and 1/80 second. Directly behind the camera body is a plate-changing back carrying 12 quarter-plates in metal sheaths and provided with an automatic counter indicating the number of the plate in position. View-finders are provided for both horizontal and vertical pictures.

880 Krügener's "Delta" camera designed by Dr. Krügener of Frankfurt on Main. British patent 1 February, 1888. Made of mahogany, for twelve 9 x 12 cm. plates. The first camera carrying the plates *inside* the instrument. They were exposed successively by means of an automatic arrangement. When the exposed plate was dropped to the bottom of the camera by means of a lever, the next plate came into position.

881 Dresser's camera manufactured by Henry Crouch, London. 1892. Behind the focusing screen of the wooden box is a storage space for three wooden double dark-slides holding quarter-plates. The camera can be used for either horizontal or vertical pictures, has view-finders for either, a lens of 5½″ focal length, iris diaphragm and clockwork shutter. A rack-and-pinion extends the front part of the camera for focusing, a pointer indicating the distance from the object.

882 "Juwel" camera. 1900. Made by Emil Wünsche A. G., Dresden. The black morocco-covered wooden box holds twelve 9 x 12 cm. plates kept in an upright position by a spring at the back of the camera. Each time a plate is moved into the focal plane by turning a handle, an indicator shows the number of the plate in position. After exposure, the plate is dropped into the bottom of the box. The lens has three diaphragms, and for slow speeds is worked by a metal disk shutter; for fast speeds a focal plane shutter is provided. Either horizontal or vertical pictures can be taken.

883 Plate magazine camera manufactured by K. van Buren, Amsterdam. c. 1900. The wooden box holds twelve 9 x 12 cm. plates kept in an upright position by a spring at the back of the camera. An automatic counter indicates the plate in position. The lens has an iris diaphragm. The camera has view-finders for horizontal and vertical pictures.

884 Plate magazine camera of English manufacture. c. 1900. The black leather-covered wooden box holds 24 3¼″ x 4¼″ plates kept in an upright position by a spring at the back of the camera. It has an automatic counter and can be used for horizontal and vertical pictures. The camera is fitted with a Beck "Primus" lens with iris diaphragm in sunk mount, and spring drop shutter giving speeds from 1 - 1/100 second.

885 Newman & Guardia's "Universal" hand camera (pattern B). London. 1903. This model is one of the earliest cameras taking square pictures, and has attached to it a plate-changing back for twelve 3¼″ x 3¼″ plates. It has a double bellows extension, Ross "Homocentric" lens F 6.3, f 5″, horizontal and vertical rising front, and a pneumatic shutter giving seven speeds, ½ - 1/100 second.

885 (a) Instruction booklet for the above camera.

886 "Frena" film magazine camera patented by J. F. Clarke in 1890 and put on the market in 1892 by R. & J. Beck & Co., London. The first magazine hand camera making use of cut celluloid film, 40 sheets 3¼″ x 4¼″ being stored in a magazine within the wooden box. After each exposure a new sheet of film is brought into position by moving a lever, which at the same time works an automatic counter. The pieces of film are notched. Photographs taken with this camera were called "Frenagraphs."

886 (a) Trade booklet entitled "Frenagraphs" containing six original photographs taken with a later and smaller model using 2¾″ x 2¾″ cut film.

(see also Nos. 923, 924)

Rollfilm Cameras

887 Kodak No. 1. 1888. The first rollfilm camera, which revolutionized camera design. Made by the Eastman (Kodak) Company, Rochester, N. Y. U. S. patent 9 May, 1888. The black leather covered wooden box contains a roll of stripping film on paper for 100 circular pictures 2½″ diameter. The

camera has a rectilinear fixed focus lens giving sharp definition of everything beyond 8 feet, has only one speed, and a fixed stop, and was the last word in simplicity in action. According to the original leather case this camera, serial No. 1321, was "presented to D. Pottinger Esq., Chief Supt. IC Railway, January, 1889."

888 Another specimen of the Kodak No. 1, serial No. 14,071, opened up to show the interior.

888 (a) *The Kodak Manual,* Rochester, 1888. With a letter dated 1 October, 1888, addressed to G. Heron Allen and signed by George Eastman.

889 Rollfilm camera "Cycle" No. 1. c. 1895, for 2¼″ x 3½″ pictures. The first model introduced by "W. K." (Krauss), Paris. Wooden box covered with black morocco leather. The drop baseboard is scaled in metres and feet. Aplanatic lens with single shutter speed, and rotating stop with three diaphragms. The number of the picture marked on the backing paper of the film could be seen through an orange window at the back of the camera.

890 Kodak "Panoram" No. 1. Patented in 1894 and introduced four years later. The special feature of this wooden camera—which was followed by smaller and larger models—was that panoramic pictures 7″ x 2¼″ could be taken on ordinary rollfilm held in the curved back, the lens mount swinging through a wide arc giving an angle of view of 112°.

891 Kodak "Panoram" No. 4, Model C. 1900. This model takes five panoramic pictures 12″ x 3½″. The Rapid Rectilinear F 10 lens gives an angle of view of 142°.

892 Kodak No. 3A folding pocket camera. Introduced in 1903, this camera model took 12 pictures 3¼″ x 5½″ and has a Bausch & Lomb Rapid Rectilinear lens. The shutter gives five speeds, time and ball.

893 Kodak Brownie No. 3 Model B. 1916. Made by the Canadian Kodak Co., Toronto. Metal box covered with imitation black morocco leather, taking rollfilm 3¾″ wide.

894 Kodak Vest Pocket Autographic camera. 1926, for 8 pictures 1⅝″ x 2½″. This light-weight aluminum camera has a fixed focus lens f 3″, and an automatic shutter for 1/25, 1/50 second, ball, and time. The tiny camera takes its name from the feature, first introduced by Kodak in 1914, enabling the title and date of the picture to be written and photographically printed on the film directly after the exposure has been made.

Press Cameras

895 "Spido" camera introduced by L. Gaumont & Co., Paris, 1900. The camera has a Zeiss anastigmat F 8, f 5⅜″, iris diaphragm and pneumatic shutter. A frame view-finder is provided for taking pictures at eye-level. A magazine holding twelve 9 x 12 cm. plates and provided with an automatic counter is attached to the camera to facilitate making exposures in quick succession.

896 Contessa "Nettel" camera introduced by Contessa Camera Works, Stuttgart, c. 1903. This light wooden camera takes 9 x 12 cm. plates and has a Zeiss 6A anastigmat f 5⅜″ in a sunk focusing mount, and focal plane shutter.

897 Contessa "Westca" camera. 1913. Manufactured by Contessa Camera Works, Stuttgart. This tiny metal vest pocket camera takes plates 1¾″ x 2¼″, and measures when closed only ¾″ deep. It was one of the smallest hand cameras on the market at the time. It has a "Detektiv Aplanat" lens F 6.8, and four shutter speeds: 1/25, 1/50, 1/100, 1/150 second.

898 "Lilliput" hand camera introduced by Heinrich Ernemann, Dresden, 1913. For plates 2⅜″ x 3½″. The camera measures only 1″ deep when closed. Anastigmat lens F 4″. The camera is intended to be used at eye-level, has a metal disk shutter and segment diaphragm for time and instantaneous exposures.

899 "Ernox" camera manufactured by the Ernemann Camera Works, Dresden, 1924. Taking 1¾″ x 2⅜″ plates, and fitted with "Ernostar" lens F 2, f 4″, focal plane shutter giving exposures 1/10 - 1/1000 second. The "Ernox," and in particular its novel wide-aperture lens, made possible for the first time reportage photography and photography at night (without flashlight). It was used by Dr. Erich Salomon for his astonishing political reportage pictures (see Nos. 711-718), by Felix H. Man (Nos. 611-614) and other pioneers of modern photo-journalism, until about 1932 when 35 mm. film was as fast as the Ilford panchromatic plates used with the "Ernox," and when fine-grain development made possible satisfactory enlargements from miniature films.

900 "Ermanox" camera introduced by the Ernemann Camera Works, Dresden, 1925. Identical to No. 899 except that this camera is fitted with the "Ernostar" lens F 1.8, f 3⅜″, which was twice as fast as the F 2 "Ernostar." However, the extremely wide aperture had the great disadvantage that the depth of focus fell off rapidly outside the focal plane, so that the camera could hardly be used at full aperture. Hence serious workers preferred the "Ernox."

901 Williamson "Pistol" camera manufactured by the Williamson Manufacturing Co., London, 1929. For plates 2¼″ x 3¼″. Ross "Xpress" lens F 4.5, f 5″. The camera takes its name from the trigger that releases the shutter.

Reflex Cameras

902 Ross "Divided" camera. This twin-lens camera was introduced by Ross & Co., London, in 1895 and takes 4″ x 5″ plates. It has two Wray lenses F 8 and a roller-blind shutter in front of the taking lens. This is the improved model with folding doors which was more compact than the original model of 1891. Made of mahogany covered with pigskin, the "Divided" was one of the earliest and best made twin-lens reflex cameras.

903 "Primus" camera. French manufacture, c. 1895. This single lens reflex camera takes 3½″ x 3½″ plates and has a Berthiot Olor lens F 5.7, f 4¾″, and focal plane shutter. When making the exposure, the release simultaneously moves the mirror up.

904 "Cambier Bolton" camera. This single lens reflex camera was designed by F. W. Mills and manufactured by W. Watson & Sons, London, 1898. Made of mahogany, it takes plates 3¼″ x 4¼″, has double extension, rising front, and a Watson "Holostigmat" (symmetrical double anastigmat) lens F 4.6, f 14½″. The camera was originally sold with a Rapid Rectilinear lens, the "Holostigmat" series being introduced in 1906. The "Extra-rapid" Thornton-Pickard focal plane shutter giving speeds up to 1/1000 second was introduced in 1898 and made the "Cambier Bolton" the fastest reflex camera at the time. On making the exposure the release automatically raises the mirror.

Detective Cameras

The desire to photograph unnoticed led to a craze between c. 1885 and 1914 for disguising cameras in all sorts of ways. Most of them were only ingenious novelties intended for amateurs.

905 Gray-Stirn waistcoat camera, 1886. Invented by Robert D. Gray of New York in 1885 and patented in the United States and Great Britain on 27 July, 1886. Manufactured by C. P. Stirn, New York. This was one of the earliest and most popular of detective cameras. The flat, circular metal instrument, 5¾″ diameter, was worn beneath the waistcoat with the fixed focus lens protruding through one of the buttonholes. Six circular pictures each 1⅝″ diameter were taken on a gelatine dry plate, which was rotated by a knob protruding through another buttonhole. The instantaneous exposures were made by pulling a string in the trouser pocket. The camera contains an original dry plate and is in the manufacturer's box.

906 "Presto" camera, 1896. Invented by Herman Casler and manufactured by E. B. Koopman, New York. This tiny metal camera looks rather like an alarm clock. It takes four 1¼″ square glass plates, or could be loaded with rollfilm for 50 exposures. It has a fixed focus lens with three diaphragms.

907 "Le Physiographe" invented by E. Bloch, 1896, and manufactured in France. Patented in Britain 1 October, 1896. The stereoscopic metal camera in the form of field-glasses contains two Rapid Rectilinear fixed focus lenses in one eye-tube at right-angles to the eye-piece which is fitted with a view-finder. The other tube forms a magazine holding 12 glass plates 4¾″ x 2″. Each of the double pictures measures 2¼″ x 2″.

The magazine still contains six original plates.

908 "Ticka" camera patented by M. Niell on 14 October, 1903, and introduced by Houghtons Ltd., London, three years later. The camera, which is in the form of a watch, takes 25 pictures on 16 mm. rollfilm. The automatic counter is coupled with the key for winding the film on. Time and instantaneous exposures could be taken with the fixed focus lens which is in the position of the winding knob of the "watch."

909 "Monocular" camera, 1910, in the form of a small hand telescope or spy-glass; of French manufacture and has a "Stylor" lens by H. Roussel, Paris, F 4.5, f 2″. Three shutter speeds, 1/25, 1/50, 1/80 second, and scale for 1 - 6 meters. The camera has a film pack holder for twelve 1¾″ x 2¼″ pictures, which are taken at right-angles to the direction in which the apparatus is pointed. Fourteen years later a similar camera was introduced by Zeiss Ikon, Germany, as the "Ergo."

910 Walking-stick camera. Introduced by A. Lehmann, Berlin, 1903. The camera itself forms the brass handle, which is hollow and acts as film magazine holding 12 film spools of 25 pictures, each measuring ¾″ x 1″. The camera measures 4½″ x 3½″ x ⅞″, and screws on to the stick. It still contains one original film on two spools. The fixed focus lens has a simple shutter, exposures being made by pulling a string. The manufacturer claimed that satisfactory enlargements up to 4″ x 5″ could be made.

911 "Petal" camera "made in occupied Japan" c. 1949. Claimed at the time to be the smallest workable camera ever made. 1⅛″ circular, ⅝″ deep; weight 70 grams. The camera is fastened to the coat lapel by a pin containing an 18″ long spring chain, so that it can be brought up to eye-level for photographing. The camera takes six circular pictures each 3/16″ diameter on a disk of film 15/16″ diameter. It is provided with a view-finder, and can be used for time and instantaneous exposures.

912 Cigaret lighter and camera made in Japan. c. 1954. Spy camera size 2¼″ x 1¾″ with fixed-focus lens F 8, taking 20 pictures 6 x 6 mm. on 8 mm. film. A strip of photographs taken with it is shown, together with an enlargement of one.

913 "Baby" camera made in Japan c. 1954. This tiny Leica-type camera size 2⅛″ x 1⅜″ with "Crystar" fixed-focus lens takes 20 pictures ½″ x ½″ on 16 mm. film.

914 "Pic" holiday snapshot camera, 1954. Introduced by Pic Distributors Ltd., Southend, England. Made of black plastic, the 3¾″ diameter circular camera takes 16 pictures, each 1⅛″ x 1½″ on 127 film. Achromatic meniscus lens and two shutters, one for instantaneous pictures (about 1/25 second) and one for time exposures. In original cardboard box with instruction leaflet.

Miscellaneous Cameras

915 Stamp camera. c. 1900. Wooden box camera of English manufacture, for quarter-plates. Takes simultaneously nine photographic "stamps" ⅞″ x 1⅛″ of one portrait on one plate. The camera has nine small meniscus lenses and the interior is divided into as many compartments. There is no shutter, but the lenses have placed in front of them a plate of metal pierced with nine small holes acting as a diaphragm. The original photograph to be copied is inserted in a metal frame facing the lenses and sliding along the base-board to vary the distance according to the size of the portrait to be copied.

916 "Royal Mail" stamp camera introduced by Butcher & Sons, London. 1907.

Wooden camera with 15 small meniscus lenses, the interior being divided into as many compartments. The shutter covering all the lenses simultaneously is controlled by a screw at the top of the camera. The pictures are taken on a 9 x 12 cm. plate and each portrait measures ⅞″ x 11/16″. In contact printing an ornamental border negative was added.

The inventor of postage stamp portraits was Pialat of Paris, c. 1862-3. In January, 1867, the idea was patented in England by William George Helsby, and there was a certain vogue during the following decades. Exhibit No. 917 comes closest to real postage stamps.

917 Perforated sheet of 24 "stamps" with G. W. Wilson's head, toned grey-green. 1888.

917 (a) 4 similar "stamps," toned red. 1888.

George Washington Wilson was photographer to Queen Victoria for Scotland. In 1888 he had the idea of printing his portrait in stamp form to be used as a seal on letters. Unfortunately a new office boy used them as postage stamps, and when the Post Office in Aberdeen missed the familiar features of Queen Victoria, the Wilson issue had to be withdrawn under threat of imprisonment for *lèse-majesté!*

918 Gordon's Micro-Photo camera c. 1890. For microscopical work. Manufactured by R. & J. Beck, London. Made of brass, with various extension tubes and a set of lenses.

STEREOSCOPY

Though a few Calotypes were taken for Wheatstone's reflecting stereoscope in 1841, stereoscopic photography began in earnest only in the mid-fifties after the introduction of Brewster's refracting stereoscope in 1851 (see also Nos. 928, 930), and in particular, of special stereoscopic cameras.

919 Dancer's binocular stereoscopic camera patented by J. B. Dancer of Manchester

on 5 September 1856 was the first stereoscopic camera put on the market, the prototype having been constructed by Dancer three years earlier. The lenses are fitted with revolving diaphragms pierced with five apertures of different sizes, which are acted upon simultaneously by rotating a brass plate mounted between the two lenses. This shutter arrangement made instantaneous photography possible for the first time.

920 F. H. Powell's single-lens stereoscopic camera registered on 27 December 1858. Manufactured by Horne & Thornthwaite, London. With this camera the two pictures are taken consecutively on the same plate. After the first picture has been taken on one half of the plate, the whole camera slides along a groove on the top of the mahogany box, and the other half of the plate is exposed. The camera movement can be varied laterally to a length of 13″, according to the distance of the object from the lens. Three wooden double slides, the focusing glass, camera and lens, all go inside the box on which the camera is mounted.

921 F. H. Powell's binocular stereoscopic camera registered on 27 December 1858. Manufactured by Horne & Thornthwaite, London. Having two lenses both pictures could be taken simultaneously, and with this camera almost instantaneous views were possible. A second pair of lenses of different focal length is provided. Three wooden double slides, the focusing glass and lens panel are all packed inside the mahogany box when not in use. The lenses have a separate storage place at the side of the box.

922 Thornton-Pickard binocular stereoscopic camera. c. 1892. For 6¾″ x 3¼″ plates. The mahogany camera has a double bellows extension, and is fitted with a Thornton-Pickard roller-blind shutter behind the lens, giving speeds up to 1/90 second. The distance between the two F 8 Rapid Rectilinear lenses can be increased to 3½″, and the lens-board can be moved a corresponding distance vertically.

923 Newman & Guardia stereoscopic magazine camera. c. 1898. For 6½″ x 4¼″ plates. The wooden camera has two Zeiss anastigmats F 6.3, f 8¼″. Iris diaphragm, vertical rising front, double extension, two view-finders. Shutter speeds ranging from ½ to 1/100 second. Attached to the camera is a magazine for 12 plates.

924 French stereoscopic magazine hand camera. c. 1900. For plates 6″ x 3″. The metal camera has two Chevalier rapid anastigmats F 7.7, iris diaphragm, adjustable pneumatic shutter. There is a view-finder and automatic changing box holding 12 plates, with counter showing the number of the plate in position.

925 "Nanna" stereoscopic hand camera. c. 1900. Metal camera of German manufacture. For plates 5″ x 2¼″. Two Rapid Rectilinear lenses, spring shutter giving various speeds up to 1/150 second. Three built-in diaphragms of different sizes. The camera, which was used at eye-level, has a sight and metal view-finder.

926 Eastman Kodak stereoscopic camera "Hawkeye" No. 4. 1901. The first hand camera for taking stereoscopic pictures on rollfilm. (3½″ wide). Shutter speeds 1-1/100 second. Made of wood.

927 Eastman Kodak "No. 2 Stereo Brownie." 1903. Made of wood, for rollfilm 3½″ wide. The lenses are opened by a wire release, have four diaphragms, and the shutter can be set for instantaneous, ball, and time exposure.
See also No. 907.

Viewing Instruments

Stereo photographs were viewed in special instruments to combine the double pictures in a relief effect. Looking at stereo pictures was as popular a pastime in the mid-nineteenth century as TV is today.

928 Refracting stereoscope c. 1853. Made of mahogany, with prismatic eye-pieces. Described by Sir David Brewster to the British Association in 1849, the instrument was first commercially produced by the Parisian scientific instrument maker Duboscq and found immediate success after its introduction at the Great Exhibition, London, 1851.

929 Lenticular stereoscope of improved design, in which the lenses can be moved laterally to suit people whose eyes are more than usually far apart. Made of walnut.

930 "Cosmorama" refracting stereoscope registered by George Knight, London, on 15 September 1854. In the form of a rosewood box on a stand, for table use. The box containing the lenses can be pushed in and out for focusing.

931 Claudet's lenticular stereoscope patented by Antoine Claudet, London, on 8 March 1855. Made of rosewood. The two eye-tubes, which can be drawn in or out to suit the viewer's eyesight, are an improvement on Brewster's design.

932 Hermagis' "opera-glass" stereoscope. 1858. Designed by Hermagis, Paris. Made of walnut, with unusually large lenses 1¾″ diameter, focused simultaneously by means of a central screw as in an opera-glass.

933 Book stereoscope patented by J. Beck, London, on 16 September 1859. This open instrument was specially designed for viewing stereoscopic illustrations in books (see Nos. 851 and 852) but could also be used for ordinary stereos. Additional light is reflected on to the pictures by a mirror. The distance of the lenses from the picture is adjustable by a rack-and-pinion.

934 Negretti and Zambra's stereoscope patented 5 December 1859. Of different construction from previous instruments: instead of the lenses being movable, the distance from them of the slide itself is adjustable. The instrument folds up into its base which is in the form of a shallow oblong wooden box.

935 Folding pocket stereoscope in the form of a shallow rosewood box, on the lines of the pocket stereo viewers for daguerreotypes (see Nos. 141 and 142).

936 Horizontal stereoscopic hand viewer of the open type invented by Oliver Wendell Holmes in 1861. Patented by Underwood & Underwood, New York, 11 June 1901. Made of wood, with aluminum eye-shield.

937 "Graphoscope" combined stereoscope and carte-de-visite viewer invented by C. J. Rowsell, 1870. In addition to viewing stereoscopic pictures as in No. 934 the big magnifying lens in the center is for viewing carte-de-visite pictures. Adjustable carriers inside the wooden box allow the height and distance of the pictures from the lenses to be varied.

938 "Le Taxiphote" patented by L. J. E. Colardeau in Paris and by J. Richard in England on 26 October 1899. The wooden cabinet brings a series of 25 stereoscopic glass slides into view in succession. A lifting frame is fed by a mechanism with a new picture each time a handle is turned. An automatic counter indicates the number of the picture in use.

Revolving Stereoscopes

939 Claudet's revolving stereoscope patented by Antoine Claudet, London, 8 March 1855. Designed for viewing albumen-on-glass transparent stereo photographs, of which it holds 80 fixed in wire frames on an endless band rotated by knobs at the side. Inside the lid of the cabinet, which can be turned up, is a mirror to reflect light through the transparent slides. Focusing of the eyepieces is effected by rack-and-pinion. This is an elegant salon instrument constructed like a piece of furniture richly inlaid with mother-of-pearl and brass, with four gilt female figures at the corners. It was shown at the Universal Exhibition in Paris, 1855.

940 Revolving stereoscope c. 1860. So designed that two people on opposite sides of the oak cabinet can simultaneously view different slides, of which 50 are mounted on an endless band.

941 Pillar stereoscope. 1863. Probably by Negretti & Zambra, London, who introduced it that year. This walnut instrument is constructed on the revolving principle similar to Nos. 939 and 940, and holds 200 slides.

942 Sawyer's "Viewmaster." This Bakelite instrument introduced by Sawyer's Inc., Portland, U.S.A., c. 1948, incorporates an entirely new system of changing the pictures. They are mounted in pairs on the perimeter of a cardboard disk, which is rotated by pressing a lever. Each disk contains seven stereo pairs in Kodachrome color.

Lenses

943 Single achromatic lens with screw-in diaphragm and focusing screw. c. 1841-2.

944 Lerebours & Secretan, Paris. Double achromatic lens No. 2895. c. 1843. With focusing screw and brass lens cap. f 9½″.

945 Lerebours & Secretan. Double achromatic lens No. 7156. c. 1847. With focusing screw and push-in diaphragm which reduces the opening from 3½″ to 2⅜″. f 14″.

946 C. Burr. Single achromatic landscape lens. c. 1845. Diameter 1⅝″, reduced by a built-in diaphragm to an effective opening of ⅞″. A pull-out stop reduces the lens opening still further to ½″. The focal length can be varied by pushing the lens in or pulling it out of a brass mount.

947 W. Ladd & Co., London. Single achromatic landscape lens. c. 1845. With screw-on lens panel.

948 Single achromatic landscape lens with focusing screw. c. 1850. f 5½″.

949 Double achromatic landscape lens c. 1855. f 5″. Plano-convex combinations with focusing screw.

950 Thomas Grubb, Dublin. Aplanatic view lens patented 8 October 1857. f 24″. Diameter 4½″. Weight 8 lbs. A diaphragm is placed in front of the lens, which also has a fixed sun-shade. With this lens construction greater covering power and rapidity was achieved than with ordinary double achromats, but it was not a true aplanat.

951 J. H. Dallmeyer, London. Single achromatic landscape lens with rotating stop, c. 1860. f 5½″.

952 Voigtländer, Braunschweig. Orthoscopic landscape lens designed by Joseph Petzval. c. 1860. f 9½″. With Waterhouse stop.

953 Voigtländer. Double achromatic portrait lens. 1862. f 24″. Diameter 5¼″. Weight 17 lbs. Still using the same lens system originally designed in 1840 by Joseph Petzval. (See No. 870.) With set of six Waterhouse stops. The lens is screwed in the original lens panel and was used for plates 16″ x 20″.

954 J. H. Dallmeyer. Achromatic triplet with Waterhouse stops. c. 1862. f 8″.

955 Thomas Ross, London. No. 5 Universal double achromatic lens for views and portraits. c. 1865. f 24″. Diameter 4¼″. Weight 5½ lbs. Waterhouse stop. The lens, which has the front combination cemented and the back combination standing free, is still constructed on the lines of the first British portrait lens made by Andrew Ross for Henry Collen in 1841.

956 Achromatic wide-angle lens. c. 1865, probably of French manufacture. f 7⅛″. Diameter 1½″. Fitted with a rotating diaphragm with five apertures of different size from F 15 to F 45.

957 S. L., Paris. "Rapide Rectilinéaire." c. 1868. Rapid rectilinear lenses were aplanats, introduced simultaneously by Steinheil in Munich and Dallmeyer in London in 1866. They were composed of two symmetrical combinations which could also be used singly, and were almost exclusively used for outdoor photography until superseded by anastigmat lenses.

958 Hermagis, Paris. "Eidoscope" aplanat No. 1. c. 1880. F 5, f 20″. Waterhouse stop. A rapid rectilinear aplanat, well corrected for chromatic and spherical aberration at large aperture.

959 Voigtländer "Euryscope" Series III. c. 1890. Portrait lens for 6¼″ x 8¼″ plates. f 11″. With Waterhouse stops. In original leather case.

960 Voigtländer "Euryscope" Series IVa. c. 1890. For portraits 16″ x 20″. f 26″. The "Euryscope" introduced in 1886 was a symmetrical aplanat of the rapid rectilinear type giving a large flat field at a much greater aperture (F 4.5 to F7) than previously possible. The "Euryscope" also had a relatively wide angle of view (70°).

961 Busch, Rathenow. "Vade Mecum" combination set No. 1 of portrait and landscape lenses. c. 1890. Consisting of 5 lenses and two supplementary lenses giving combinations of varying focal lengths from 4″ to 30″. In original leather case, with printed instructions in English.

962 C. P. Goerz, Berlin. Wide-angle "Lynkeioscope" series F No. 3. c. 1895. Aplanat f 8½″. Five rotating stops.

963 A. Watkins, London. "Pinhole lens" c. 1900. Not a lens but simply a tiny hole pierced in a metal disc. Many scientists from Sir David Brewster in the mid-fifties onward argued that a pinhole gives much truer perspective because it is free from the aberrations produced by lenses. It was not until after the introduction of fast gelatine dry plates that photographing without a lens became possible and was put forward again by René Colson (1891). Only a few cranks practiced it, for the exposure time in sunshine was approximately twenty minutes.

964 Sets of lens stops in their original leather cases.

Shutters

965 Dancer revolving diaphragm with three apertures of different sizes and lens flap acting as shutter. Patented by J. B. Dancer on 5 September 1856. The revolving diaphragm is pushed on to the lens like a lens-cap. The actual lens opening at full aperture is only ⅞″.

966 Cadett instantaneous view shutter introduced by Marion & Co., London, 1878. The introduction of fast dry plates necessitated quick-acting shutters. This clumsy and heavy iron shutter, which can be set for twelve speeds, consists of a revolving disc released by a pneumatic bulb.

967 Lancaster revolving disc shutter patented 1 May, 1885. The shutter is screwed on to the lens. A metal disc which revolves by means of a rubber band acts as shutter when released, the speed depending on the tightening of the rubber band.

968 A. S. Newman pneumatic guillotine shutter patented on 27 May, 1886. The shutter, which was introduced by the London Stereoscopic Co., is screwed in front of the lens. The exposures ranging from 1 - 1/100 second are marked round a tube containing compressed air. The guillotine blade drops according to the speed set on the regulating valve.

969 Caldwell instantaneous shutter introduced by W. Wray, London, 1888. Screwed in front of the lens, the shutter gives five speeds and time exposure.

970 Bausch & Lomb pneumatic shutter patented 6 January, 1891, made for the Eastman Kodak Co. Gives time and instantaneous exposures down to 1/100 second.

971 P. & E. F. Wallis roller-blind shutter, patented 24 October, 1899. Screwed on to the outside of the lens, the roller-blind can be set for five speeds from 1/15 to 1/90 second.

Light Meters

972 Louis Bing actinometer patented 13 September, 1866. To determine the exposure in positive printing with carbon tissues. The rosewood box has a tinted glass lid divided into eight squares of equal size numbered from 1 to 8 in the ratio in which the transparency of the glass decreases. For measuring the light intensity, a strip of sensitive paper is inserted in the bottom of the box containing a pressure frame which keeps the sensitive paper pressed against the numbers.

973 Walter Woodbury actinometer. 1879. To determine the exposure for printing Woodburytypes. Manufactured by Sciopticon Co., London. A circular metal box containing a disc with colored segments of various shades of brown, under a protective glass. The sensitive paper to be matched is inserted through a slot.

974 Alfred Watkins "Standard" exposure meter patented 27 January, 1890. Manufactured by R. Field & Co., Birmingham. A brass cylinder with rotating scales covering all the necessary calculations. The light intensity was measured by pointing the end of the tube containing sensitive paper towards the source of light and timing the number of seconds needed to darken the paper to a standard tint. The instrument carried sufficient paper for several hundred tests. The seconds were measured by swinging the cylinder on an attached chain, as a pendulum, each double swing lasting one second.

975 Scott exposure calculator patented 4 October, 1892, and made by the Britannia Works Co. (since 1900 Ilford Ltd.). A simplification of the original Hurter and Driffield actinograph, in the form of five rotatable concentric aluminum rings marked with various data figures from which the exposure could be calculated on the principle of the slide rule.

976 Alfred Watkins "Bee" meter patented 22 December, 1895. This meter in the form of a watch used a strip of light-sensitive paper from which, by means of the Watkins Speed Card, the exposure could be calculated. This inexpensive exposure meter was a great favorite with amateurs, being manufactured until the mid-1930's.

977 Wynne "Infallible" Hunter meter patented September, 1919. A very similar calculator to No. 979, with 8-page printed table of plate speeds.

978 Heyde "Aktino-Photometer," 1905. Heyde's rotating wedge meter of German manufacture is the first visual exposure meter. The subject is observed through a blue filter with varied depth of color. The meter was rotated until only the highlights of the subject were visible, when the exposure marked on the scale was read off.

979 Contessa Nettel "Diaphot" light calculator. 1922. Incorporates a set of tables from which the exposure could be calculated.

980 Pickard light meter c. 1929. A visual meter in the form of a tube with an eye-cup. When held to the eye and pointed towards the subject, numbers are seen; by rotating and choosing the last visible number, the exposure can be calculated from a table.

Other Accessories

981 View-finder and focusing glass combined. c. 1870. To be screwed on to the camera. The image is thrown on to a small circular ground-glass which has a hood, to give a clear image even in bright daylight. The bi-convex lens also serves as a focusing glass.

It had been a great *desideratum* of photographers, especially amateurs, to be able to take a large number of photographs consecutively on a roll of sensitized paper. The first such device was constructed by A. J. Melhuish and J. B. Spencer in 1854. Melhuish's roll-holder took 12 pictures 12" x 15" on sensitized waxed paper, but owing to its clumsiness was little used. Leon Warnerke introduced an excellent roll-holder in 1875, allowing 100 pictures to be taken on stripping film. But it was only George Eastman's mass-production methods, and the demands of the greatly increased ranks of amateurs, that made the commercial introduction of the roller-slide practicable.

982 Eastman/Walker roller-slide, 1887. A separate magazine of rollfilm to be attached to the camera, before the introduction of rollfilm cameras. For stripping film 4" wide, allowing 24 4" x 5" pictures. Patented 5 May, 1885, the original roller-slide was made of metal; the lighter mahogany model shown was introduced in 1887.

983 Adams & Co. roller-slide. c. 1905. This attachment was for daylight loading of celluloid rollfilm 3¼" wide. To facilitate the reading of film numbers the roller-slide is fitted with an orange glass window with a magnifying glass over it.

984 Newman plate changing box, improved model patented by A. S. Newman on 30 July, 1892. A plate magazine holding twelve 5" x 7" dry plates each in a separate sheath. After exposure a fresh plate was manipulated into the focal plane through a soft leather bag on top. An indicator on the back of the magazine shows the number of the plate in position.

985 Gaumont, Paris. Plate magazine for "Spido" stereo camera, c. 1900. The magazine contains 12 sheaths for plates 2⅜" x 5⅛", and has an automatic counter indicating the plate in position.

986 "New Patent Jewel Kaleidoscope" made by the London Stereoscopic Co. c. 1860. Sir David Brewster's invention patented on 10 July, 1817, found immediate favor and remained a scientific toy throughout the 19th century. The most beautiful of all later modifications was the "Jewel" kaleidoscope containing, in addition to the usual pieces of colored glass and wire, small tubes partly filled with colored liquid, producing jewel-like effects, which constantly form new hexagonal patterns on turning the rotating wheel. The kaleidoscope tube with two mirrors inclined to each other at an angle of 60°, is fixed on a typical mid-Victorian iron stand.

987 Rotating Kaleidoscope c. 1860. Of different construction from Brewster's. Instead of loose pieces of colored glass being viewed by transmitted light, solid objects such as pieces of colored material, feathers, shells etc. are fixed on a revolving cylinder in a box and viewed by reflected light admitted through a ground-glass window in one side of the box. By turning the handle of the cylinder, pushing it further in, or pulling it out, constantly changing effects are reflected by the mirrors in the tube, set at right-angles to the cylinder.

COLOR PHOTOGRAPHY

The wish to take color pictures was felt from the very beginning of photography, but though various methods were tried, color photography became practicable only in the 1890's after the introduction of orthochromatic and soon afterwards panchromatic dry plates.

988 Frederic Eugene Ives, Philadelphia. Stereoscopic "Kromskop" camera, 1891. Mahogany. Three separation negatives were taken in rapid succession on one plate by means of a repeating back containing red, green and blue-violet filters. After development, a diapositive was made from the plate by contact printing, and this was cut into its three monochrome separations, called "Kromogram," which appeared in color when viewed in the "Kromskop."

989 F. E. Ives. Stereoscopic "Kromskop" (originally called "Photochromoscope"). Invented in 1892, U. S. Patent 18 December, 1894. Mahogany. Made by the Photochromoscope Syndicate Ltd., London, 1895. The monochrome diapositives taken with Ives' stereoscopic "Kromskop" camera (No. 988) are viewed through a green, a red, and a blue-violet filter arranged in step form on a frame. The instrument is provided with a reflecting mirror and a ground-glass to give even illumination, and has an eye-shield to keep out extraneous light.

990 A selection of stereo "Kromograms" taken by Ives, showing still-life and landscapes. These monochrome slides when viewed in the "Kromskop" appear as perfect color pictures in relief.

991 F. E. Ives. Single-lens "Kromskop," 1892. Mahogany. Made by the Photochromoscope Syndicate Ltd., London. For those who did not wish to see the pictures in relief or to buy a special camera, Ives constructed the ordinary or "Junior Kromskop" for viewing pictures taken with an ordinary camera fitted with a "Kromskop" repeating back, which could be bought separately. The construction of the "Junior Kromskop" is in all other respects the same as No. 989.

992 A selection of "Kromograms" for the "Junior Kromskop."

993 F. E. Ives. Projection "Kromskop," 1895. Mahogany. Constructed by Newton & Co., London. For the projection of "Kromskop" color photographs Ives invented this instrument for use with an ordinary magic lantern. The three diapositives are superimposed by means of this triple projection instrument containing a red, a green, and a blue-violet filter behind three adjustable projection lenses.

994 F. E. Ives/R. W. Wood Diffraction Chromoscope, 1900. Wood. This instrument was designed by Ives for Prof. R. W. Wood of Wisconsin. Wood's method of producing color photographs by diffraction (British patent 2 March, 1899) was novel. Three negatives were taken through red, green, and blue filters in the usual manner, and from these, diapositives were made. Each positive has superimposed on it a different diffraction screen: 2000 lines per inch for red, 2400 for green and 2750 for blue. The three diapositives are then printed together in register to form a final picture 3¼" x 3¼" which is perfectly transparent and merely consists of a diffraction screen with variable spacing. When this transparency is viewed in the diffraction Chromoscope, the wave lengths of the light pass through the corresponding lines and form a perfect color picture.

995 E. T. Butler. One-shot color camera. British patent 11 December, 1897. For 3¼" x 4¼" plates. An early camera for taking the three separation negatives simultaneously. The light passing through the lens is partly reflected by a greenish-blue filter and passes through a red filter onto plate 1; some light passing through the greenish-blue filter is reflected by a yellow filter and passes through a blue-violet filter onto plate 2; and that part of the light that is transmitted through the yellow filter passes through a green filter onto plate 3.

996 Louis Ducos du Hauron. "Le Mélano-chromoscope." British patent 1 August, 1899. For taking three-color negatives simul-taneously and for subsequently viewing dia-positives from them in color. The morocco-leather-covered wooden box is divided into three compartments. The light rays passing through a lens near the bottom of the box are reflected by a mirror and split into three beams of light, passing through as many lenses and colored filters—blue, magenta and green, on to the sensitive plate.

997 Packets of Autochrome plates.

The brothers Auguste and Louis Lumière invented in 1903 the first completely satis-factory color-screen process, which they called Autochrome. The plates were manu-factured at their own factory at Lyons and introduced in 1907. The glass plates were coated with fine grains of red, green and blue dyed starch, over which a thin film of panchromatic gelatine emulsion was applied. The plates were supplied in sizes for any standard camera, and the exposure was made through the glass side of the plate, and hence through the color grain base, resulting in a direct positive transparency.

FORERUNNERS OF CINEMATOGRAPHY

The cinema has its origin in the entertain-ment with the magic lantern, an instrument which was known by 1650, and fully described and illustrated by Athanasius Kircher in the second edition of his book *Ars Magna Lucis et Umbrae,* 1671. In the late eighteenth and early nineteenth century E. G. Robertson in Paris produced elaborate and sensational shows with various pro-jection effects, which he called "Phantas-magoria." In 1839 Henry Langdon Childe invented for these magic lantern shows dissolving views, chromatropes, and other movable slides, in which two or more pictures painted on separate glass slides were superimposed and movement given by turning a handle. Favorite slides of this kind were "Ship leaving harbor," a trapeze acrobat, "artificial fireworks," etc.

998 A selection of *movable magic lantern slides,* 1840-1860.

The Thaumotrope, the first toy demon-strating persistence of vision, was invented in 1825 by Dr. W. H. Fitton of London, based on a demonstration by Sir John Herschel of a spinning coin in which head and tail can be seen at the same time. Dr. J. A. Paris described and illustrated the thaumotrope in his book *Philosophy in Sport made Science in Earnest* (London, Vol. III, 1827) and at the same time had the toy made for sale.

999 A wooden box marked "Optical De-lusion Cards" containing 10 *thaumotrope* discs of cardboard with hand-colored pic-tures, different on each side, and strings attached for rotating them, as illustrated on the lid of the box.

In 1832 Joseph Plateau of Ghent and Simon Stampfer of Vienna independently invented the phenakistiscope and stroboscope re-spectively, based on some observations of

Michael Faraday the previous year concerning moving wheels. On the perimeter of a slotted cardboard disc of 7¼″ - 9¾″ diameter are hand-colored printed figures in various phases of a movement. By spinning the disc and observing through the slots the pictures reflected in a mirror, the illusion of movement is given. At a later date, unslotted discs were introduced and the movement observed through a second plain disc with slots.

1000   A selection of *phenakistiscope* and *stroboscope* discs, 1833.

In 1833 W. G. Horner of Bristol invented a variation on the same principle, the Daedalium, a slotted revolving drum with strips of paper round the inside with figures on them. This type of instrument was patented in Great Britain by P. H. Desvignes on 27 February, 1860. Since 1866 the instrument is commonly known as the Zoetrope, the name given it by William E. Lincoln of Providence, who took out a U. S. patent on 23 April, 1867.

1001   *Zoetrope* c. 1860. Made by Carpenter & Westley, London. Diameter of drum 29 cm. 11½″. Containing picture bands to go around the inside of the drum, and picture discs to lie at the bottom of the drum, enabling the viewer to see two sets of moving pictures at the same time.

1002   *"Wheel of Life"* patented by Thomas Ross, London, 10 October, 1871. This instrument was designed for projecting animated painted figures, or photographs, by the magic lantern. It consists of two discs which revolve in opposite directions on turning a handle: one transparent bearing the pictures, the other opaque, with a slot, acting as a shutter. The shutter disc revolves much faster than the picture disc.

1003   *"Tachyscope,"* introduced by Ottomar Anschütz, Posen. 1887. The drum, which can be used vertically or horizontally, is very shallow compared with the Zoetrope. The cardboard picture band is slotted and itself forms the wall of the drum. In the older form of Zoetrope the drawings were made to suit the number of slots in the drum, but Anschütz's picture bands were copied from his photographs of animals and people in motion, and each picture series required its own particular number of slots to complete the cycle of phases of movement. The eight cardboard picture bands include a flying stork, bucking donkey, jumping horse, trotting horse, marching soldier, running athlete. Each has printed on it "Ottomar Anschütz, Posen."

1004   *"Kinematador."* c. 1885. The idea of the German instrument is very close to Muybridge's Zoopraxiscope. It may count as another forerunner of cinematographic projection apparatus, except that it projects animated hand-drawn and colored pictures, not photographs. These are arranged round a rotating celluloid disc 5½″ diameter, with intermittent shutter. The projection panel is interchangeable so that ordinary lantern slides could also be projected by the apparatus.

EARLY CINEMATOGRAPHY

The brothers Auguste and Louis Lumière designed in 1895 the first really practicable and satisfactory cinematograph taking and projecting apparatus, which they called "Le Cinématographe." With it they gave the first public cinema show in France to a paying audience at the Salon Indien of the Grand Café, 14 Boulevard des Capucines, Paris, on 28 December, 1895. From 1896 onward the "Cinématographe" was commercially produced, and with it the first cinema shows were given in many countries, including England and Australia.

1005   Auguste and Louis Lumière. *Description of the Cinematographe,* London, 1896. The 34-page description, illustrated with woodcuts, was sent out with the apparatus by the London agent of the Lumières.

1006   Program of the first cinema performance in Australia, put on by Marius Sestier, agent of the Lumière brothers, at the Lyceum

Theatre, Sydney, on 26 September, 1896. Sestier has written on the program the kind of music he desired to accompany the films.

1007 Bronze medal issued by the French Mint to commemorate the 50th anniversary of Lumière's cinematography, 1895-1945. 63 mm. diameter. The design by R. B. Baron shows on one side a film spool and on the other a portrait of Louis Lumière.

1008 *"Kinora."* Invented by A. and L. Lumière. British patent 19 October, 1896. In this home viewing instrument a series of about 250 photographs taken by Lumière's cinematograph camera are mounted radially from an axle on flexible supports. When the cylinder is rotated by turning the handle, each picture is arrested momentarily by a stop, thus allowing it to be seen distinctly through the magnifying lens provided, and then permitting it to fly into its normal radial position as the rotation of the axle sets its edge free.

1009 Six *"Kinora"* reels: dancing Scot, elephant and keeper, monkey and keeper, horse tamer, two comedians, pillow-fight.

1010 Another more elaborate *"Kinora"* model on an iron base. The reel is enclosed in an iron case, daylight being reflected on to the pictures through an opening containing a mirror.

1011 4 *"Kammatograph"* glass discs for projection in L. U. Kamm's cinematographic camera-projector. British patent 17 March, 1898. 270 - 300 photographs are arranged spirally on the 12″ diameter disc, with center hole. In projection, the disc is given intermittent rotary motion and a gradual horizontal movement. Running time 30-40 seconds. Boxing match, two little girls dancing, another dance, a paddle steamer.

1012 *"Olikos"* cine-camera. French manufacture, c. 1897-8. A 2½″ x 3½″ glass plate is rapidly moved upwards and sideways across the lens opening behind a segment shutter, taking in all 84 photographs each 8 x 7 mm. The camera has a fixed focus lens normally used at full aperture, though two different diaphragm stops are provided, and also a different segment shutter. An indicator on the outside of the leather-covered wooden box records how many pictures have been taken. An optical view-finder is fixed on top of the camera.

1013 *"Electric Gyroscope"* cine-camera. British patents 1908 and 1911. This cine-camera was electrically driven by a dynamo started by a built-in 16-volt battery. A small, powerful gyroscope counteracted any slight oscillation. Takes 300 feet of standard film, with automatic indicator showing how much film has been shot. The number of frames per second can be varied from 10 to 25.

1014 *"Aeroscope"* cine-camera invented by K. de Prozynski and bearing his autograph signature. British patents 12 March, 1910, and 25 April, 1912. Manufactured by Cherry Kearton, the famous bird photographer. Takes 450 feet of standard film. The mechanism is driven by compressed air stored in a small reservoir with pressure-gauge, one charge by an ordinary bicycle pump being sufficient to expose the entire length of film. As in No. 1013, the number of frames per second can be varied. The "Aeroscope" also had a gyroscope. With automatically driven cine-cameras such as 1013 and 1014, far better uniformity of exposure was attained than by a crank.

1015 *"Malma"* home cinema manufactured by Maltheser Maschinenbau, Berlin. c. 1910. For taking and projecting films. Hugo Meyer "Kinon" lens F 3. 2, f 35 mm., stops and iris. Film-winding system marked in meters and feet.

1016 *Pathé home cinema projector* patented by Pathé Frères, Paris, 1908-9. The film is crank driven, and this movement gives power to a dynamo feeding an electric bulb illuminating the film. There are 14 Pathé films each 28 mm. wide and 300 - 500 feet long. Pathé were at the time the largest film producers in the world, with a daily output of 80 miles. The films include comedies, a bullfight, a dragonfly, fire-fighting, etc.

BOOKS RECOMMENDED FOR FURTHER STUDY OF CREATIVE PHOTOGRAPHY

For a complete bibliography see Gernsheim, Helmut, *Creative Photography*.

General Works

Freund, Giselle: *La photographie en France au dix-neuvième siècle: Essai de sociologie et d'esthétique*. Paris 1936. 154 pp. illus.

Gernsheim, Helmut: *Masterpieces of Victorian Photography*. London 1951. 107 pp. incl. 72 pl.

Gernsheim, Helmut: *Creative Photography: 1839-1960*. London & Boston, U.S.A. 1962. 258 pp. incl. 244 illus.

Gernsheim, Helmut and Alison: *The History of Photography from the Earliest Use of the Camera Obscura in the Eleventh Century up to 1914*. London & New York. 1955. 395 pp. and 359 illus.

Lécuyer, Raymond: *Histoire de la photographie*. Paris 1945. 452 pp. incl. approx. 500 illus.

Newhall, Beaumont: *The History of Photography from 1839 to the Present Day*. New York. 1949. 256 pp. incl. 163 illus.

Newhall, Beaumont and Nancy: *Masters of Photography*. New York 1958. 192 pp. incl. 150 illus.

Pollack, Peter: *The Picture History of Photography from the Earliest Beginnings to the Present Day*. New York 1958. 624 pp. incl. 600 illus.

Whiting, John R.: *Photography Is a Language*. New York 1946. 142 pp. incl. illus.

Monographs on and Autobiographies of Leading Photographers Who Are Represented in the Exhibition

Atget, Eugène: *Atget* by Camille Recht. Paris & Leipzig 1930. 34 pp. and 96 pl.

Bayard, Hippolyte: *Bayard* by Lo Duca. Paris 1943. 30 pp. and 48 pl.

Beaton, Cecil: *Photobiography*. London 1951. 254 pp. incl. 60 pl.

Boord, W. Arthur (editor): *Sun Artists*. London 1891. 62 pp. and 32 pl. Contains monographs on H. P. Robinson, Sawyer, Cameron, B. Gay Wilkinson, etc.

Brandt, Bill: *Camera in London*. London 1948. 88 pp. incl. 58 pl.

Brassaï: *Brassaï* by Henry Miller and Brassaï. Paris 1952. 76 pp. incl. 60 pl.

Cameron, J. M.: *Julia Margaret Cameron: Her Life and Photographic Work* by Helmut Gernsheim. London 1948. 85 pp. and 55 pl.

Carroll, Lewis: *Lewis Carroll — Photographer* by Helmut Gernsheim. London & New York 1950. 138 pp. and 64 pl.

Cartier-Bresson, H.: *The Photographs of Henri Cartier-Bresson* by Lincoln Kirstein and Beaumont Newhall. New York 1947. 56 pp. incl. 41 pl.

Daguerre, L. J. M.: *L. J. M. Daguerre: the History of the Diorama and the Daguerreotype* by Helmut and Alison Gernsheim. London & New York 1956. 220 pp. and 64 pl.

Evans, Walker: *American Photographs by Walker Evans* by Lincoln Kirstein. New York 1938. 200 pp. incl. 87 pl.

Fenton, Roger: *Roger Fenton, Photographer of the Crimean War* by Helmut and Alison Gernsheim. London & New York 1954. 116 pp. and 64 pl.

Genthe, Arnold: *As I Remember*. New York 1937. 290 pp. and 112 illus.

Gernsheim, Helmut: *The Man Behind the Camera*. London 1948. 144 pp. incl. 54 illus. Contains chapters on Beaton, Gernsheim, Hoppé, McBean, Felix H. Man, Parsons, Suschitzky, etc.

Hill, D. O.: *David Octavius Hill, Master of Photography* by Heinrich Schwarz. London & New York 1932. 61 pp. and 80 pl.

Hoppé, E. O.: *Hundred Thousand Exposures*. London 1945. 229 pp. incl. 64 pl.

Hutton, Kurt: *Speaking Likeness*. London 1947. 88 pp. incl. 58 pl.

Martin, Paul: *Victorian Snapshots*. London 1939. 72 pp. and 79 pl.

Nadar (Gaspard Felix Tournachon). *Quand j'étais photographe*. Paris n.d. (1899). 312 pp.

Ray, Man: *Man Ray: Photographs 1920-1934*. Hertford, U.S.A. 1934. 10 pp. and 104 plates.

Salomon, Dr. Erich: *Berühmte Zeitgenossen in unbewachten Augenblicken*. Stuttgard 1931. 48 pp. and 112 illus.

Steichen, Edward: *Edward Steichen* by Carl Sandburg. New York 1929. Illus.

Stieglitz, Alfred: *America and Alfred Stieglitz: a Collective Portrait* (a symposium). New York 1934. 339 pp. and 32 pl.

Strand, Paul: *Paul Strand, Photographs 1915-1945* by Nancy Newhall. New York 1945. 32 pp. incl. 23 pl.

Weston, Edward: *Edward Weston* by Nancy Newhall. New York 1946. 36 pp. incl. 23 pl.

——*The Day-books of Edward Weston* edited by Nancy Newhall. Part I, Rochester, New York 1962.

BOOKS WHICH ARE INFORMATIVE CONCERNING VARIOUS PERIODS IN CREATIVE PHOTOGRAPHY:

"Fine Art" Photography

Guest, Antony: *Art and the Camera*. London 1907. 159 pp. Illus.

Hinton, A. Horsley: *Practical Pictorial Photography*. London 1910. Part I, 108 pp., Part II, 69 pp. Illus.

Petit, Pierre A., junior: *La photographie artistique*. Paris 1883. 46 pp.

Robinson, Henry Peach: *Pictorial Effect in Photography*. London 1869. 199 pp. Illus.

——*Picture Making by Photography*. London 1884. 146 pp. Illus.

——*The Elements of a Pictorial Photograph*. London 1896. 167 pp. Illus.

Schintling, Karl von: *Kunst und Photographie*. Berlin 1927. 68 pp. Illus.

Tilney, F. C.: *The Principles of Photographic Pictorialism*. Boston 1930. 218 pp. and 80 pl.

Wall, A. H.: *Artistic Landscape Photography*. London 1896. 171 pp. Illus.

Naturalistic Photography

Emerson, P. H.: *Naturalistic Photography for Students of the Art*. London 1889. 307 pp.

Impressionistic Photography

Bourgeois, Paul (editor): *Esthétique de la photographie*. Paris 1900. 96 pp. Illus.

Demachy, Robert, and Puyo, C.: *Les procédés d'art en photographie*. Paris 1906. 146 pp. and 42 pl.

Doty, Robert: *Photo-Secession; Photography as a Fine Art*. Rochester, New York 1960. 104 pp. incl. 32 pl.

Holme, Charles: *Art in Photography*. London 1905. 60 pp. and 112 pl.

Loescher, Fritz: *Die Bildnisphotographie*. Berlin (n.d.) c. 1925.

Matthies-Masuren, F. R.: *Künstlerische Photographie: Entwicklung und Einfluss in Deutschland*. Berlin 1907. 117 pp. Illus.

Puyo, C.: *Notes sur la photographie artistique*. Paris 1896. 51 pp. Illus.

Sauvel, Edouard: *De la propriété artistique en photographie*. Paris 1897. 126 pp.

Sizeranne, R. de la: *La photographie, est-elle un art?* Paris 1899. 51 pp. Illus.

Bauhaus and New Objectivity

Gernsheim, Helmut: *New Photo Vision*. London 1942. 32 pp. and 32 pl.

Gräff, Werner: *Es kommt der neue Photograph*. Berlin 1929. 126 pp. Illus.

Lerski, Helmar: *Köpfe des Alltags*. Introduction by Curt Glaser. Berlin 1931. 10 pp. and 80 pl.

Moholy-Nagy, Laszlo: *Malerei, Photographie, Film*. Munich 1925. 132 pp., approx. 80 illus.

L. Moholy-Nagy: 60 Fotos. Edited and introduced by Franz Roh. Berlin 1930.

Renger-Patzsch, Albert: *Die Welt ist schön*. Edited and introduced by Carl Georg Heise. Munich 1928. 22 pp. and 100 pl.

Roh, Franz: *Foto-Eye: 76 Photographs of Our Time*. Ed. by Franz Roh and Jan Tschichold and with an introduction by Franz Roh on "Mechanism and Expression." Stuttgart 1929.

Sander, August: *Antlitz der Zeit*. Introduction by Alfred Döblin. Munich 1929. 17 pp. and 60 pl.

ILLUSTRATIONS

Cover picture: **Julia Margaret Cameron.** "Florence." 1872.

1. **Nicéphore Niépce.** The world's first photograph. 1826.
2. **W. H. Fox Talbot.** "The Open Door." 1844.
3. **David Octavius Hill and Robert Adamson.** Sailors at Newhaven near Edinburgh. c. 1845.
4. **William Telfer.** Daguerreotype of a lady. c. 1849.
5. **Antoine Claudet.** Stereoscopic daguerreotype, "The Geography Lesson." 1851.
6. **Alois Löcherer.** Transport of the "Bavaria," Munich 1850.
7. **Roger Fenton.** Domes of the Cathedral of the Resurrection in the Kremlin. 1852.
8. **Robert MacPherson.** Garden of the Villa d'Este, Tivoli. c. 1857.
9. **Henry White.** Bramble and ivy. c. 1856.
10. **James Robertson.** Crimean War: Interior of the Redan, Sebastopol, after the Russian withdrawal, September 1855.
11. **Robert Howlett.** I. K. Brunel. 1857.
12. **Lewis Carroll.** "It Won't Come Smooth" (Irene MacDonald). 1863.
13. **O. G. Rejlander.** Street urchins. c. 1857.
14. **James Anderson.** Base of Trajan Column, Rome. c. 1858.
15. **Carlo Ponti.** Courtyard of the Doge's Palace, Venice. c. 1860.
16. **Thomas Annan.** David Livingstone. 1864.
17. **Julia Margaret Cameron.** Sir John Herschel. 1867.
18. **P. H. Delamotte.** Rebuilding of the Crystal Palace at Sydenham. 1853.
19. **William Draper.** Boy with parrots. c. 1865.
20. Franco-Prussian War. Blown-up bridge near Mézières. August 1870.
21. **T. H. O'Sullivan.** "The Harvest of Death." Battlefield of Gettysburg, July 1863.
22. **H. P. Robinson.** "Dawn," detail from "Dawn and Sunset." 1885.
23. **Viscountess Hawarden.** At the window. c. 1864.
24. **Nadar.** Baron Taylor. c. 1865.
25. **Etienne Carjat.** Gioachino Rossini. c. 1865.
26. **John Thomson.** Poor woman and baby. 1876.
27. **Lyddell Sawyer.** In the Castle Garth, Newcastle. 1888.
28. **P. H. Emerson.** "Taking up the eel-net." 1885.
29. Paris World Exhibition 1889. Under the Eiffel Tower.
30. **Eadweard Muybridge.** Race horse. 1884-85.
31. **Alfred Stieglitz.** Going to the post. 1904.
32. **Frau E. Nothmann.** In the garden. c. 1897.
33. **Robert Demachy.** "Primavera." 1898.
34. **Eugène Atget.** Tree roots at St. Cloud. c. 1910.
35. **E. O. Hoppé.** Manhattan from Brooklyn Bridge. 1919.
36. **Albert Renger-Patzsch.** Crab fisherwoman. 1927.
37. **Cecil Beaton.** Jean Cocteau. 1936.
38. **Edward Steichen.** Paul Robeson as "The Emperor Jones." 1933.
39. **Erich Salomon.** Aristide Briand points at Dr. Salomon at a banquet at the Quai d'Orsay, to which Salomon had not been admitted. 1931.
40. **Arthur Rothstein.** Dust storm, Cimarron County, Oklahoma. 1936.
41. **Dorothea Lange.** Migrant landworker's wife and children. 1936.
42. **Henri Cartier-Bresson.** Sunday on the banks of the Marne. 1938.
43. **Kurt Hutton.** At the fair. 1938.
44. **Edward Weston.** Paprica. 1930.
45. **Man Ray.** Solarisation. 1931.
46. **L. Moholy-Nagy.** Photogram. 1922.
47. **Harold E. Edgerton.** Splash of milk resulting from a drop of milk. 1936.
48. **Winifred Casson.** Surrealist composition. c. 1935.

1. **Nicéphore Niépce.** The world's first photograph. 1826.

2. **W. H. Fox Talbot.** "The Open Door." 1844.

3. **David Octavius Hill and Robert Adamson.** Sailors at Newhaven near Edinburgh. c. 1845

4. **William Telfer.** Daguerreotype of a lady. c. 1849.

5. **Antoine Claudet.** Stereoscopic daguerreotype, "The Geography Lesson." 1851.

6. **Alois Löcherer.** Transport of the "Bavaria," Munich 1850.

7. **Roger Fenton.** Domes of the Cathedral of the Resurrection in the Kremlin. 1852.

8. **Robert MacPherson.** Garden of the Villa d'Este, Tivoli. c. 1857.

9. **Henry White.** Bramble and ivy. c. 1856.

10. **James Robertson.** Crimean War: Interior of the Redan, Sebastopol, after the Russian withdrawal, September 1855.

11. Robert Howlett. I. K. Brunel. 1857.

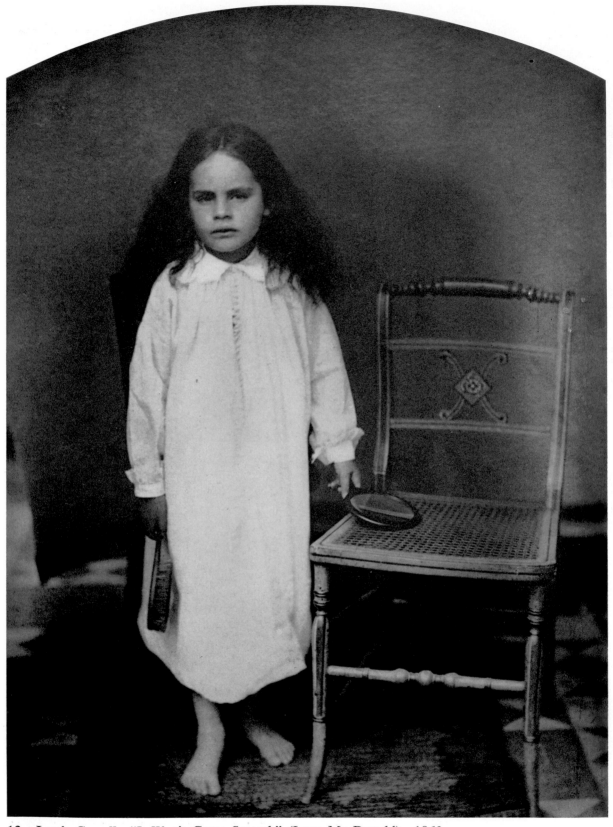

12. **Lewis Carroll.** "It Won't Come Smooth" (Irene MacDonald). 1863.

13. **O. G. Rejlander.** Street urchins. c. 1857.

14. **James Anderson.** Base of Trajan Column, Rome. c. 1858.

15. **Carlo Ponti.** Courtyard of the Doge's Palace, Venice. c. 1860.

16. **Thomas Annan.** David Livingstone. 1864.

17. **Julia Margaret Cameron.** Sir John Herschel. 1867.

18. **P. H. Delamotte.** Rebuilding of the Crystal Palace at Sydenham. 1853.

19. **William Draper.** Boy with parrots. c. 1865.

20. Franco-Prussian War. Blown-up bridge near Mézières. August 1870.

21. **T. H. O'Sullivan.** "The Harvest of Death." Battlefield of Gettysburg, July 1863.

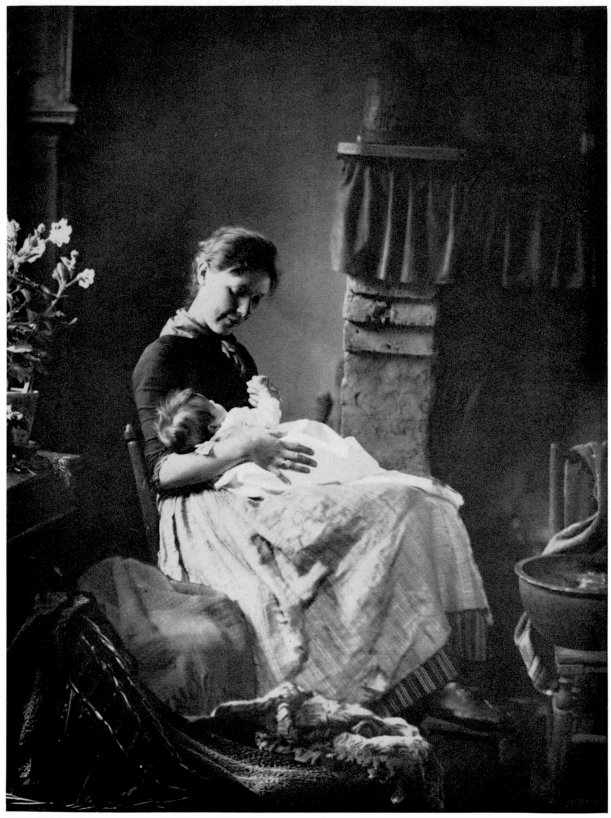

22. **H. P. Robinson.** "Dawn," detail from "Dawn and Sunset." 1885.

23. **Viscountess Hawarden.** At the window. c. 1864.

24. **Nadar.** Baron Taylor. c. 1865.

25. **Etienne Carjat.** Gioachino Rossini. c. 1865.

26. **John Thomson.** Poor woman and baby. 1876.

27. **Lyddell Sawyer.** In the Castle Garth, Newcastle. 1888.

28. **P. H. Emerson.** "Taking up the eel-net." 1885.

29. Paris World Exhibition 1889. Under the Eiffel Tower.

30. **Eadweard Muybridge.** Race horse. 1884-85.

31. **Alfred Stieglitz.** Going to the post. 1904.

32. **Frau E. Nothmann.** In the garden. c. 1897.

33. **Robert Demachy.** "Primavera." 1898.

34. **Eugène Atget.** Tree roots at St. Cloud. c. 1910.

35. **E. O. Hoppé.** Manhattan from Brooklyn Bridge. 1919.

36. **Albert Renger-Patzsch.** Crab fisherwoman. 1927.

37. **Cecil Beaton.** Jean Cocteau. 1936.

38. **Edward Steichen.** Paul Robeson as "The Emperor Jones." 1933.

39. **Erich Salomon.** Aristide Briand points at Dr. Salomon at a banquet at the Quai d'Orsay, to which Salomon had not been admitted. 1931.

40. **Arthur Rothstein.** Dust storm, Cimarron County, Oklahoma. 1936.

41. **Dorothea Lange.** Migrant landworker's wife and children. 1936.

42. **Henri Cartier-Bresson.** Sunday on the banks of the Marne. 1938.

43. **Kurt Hutton.** At the fair. 1938.

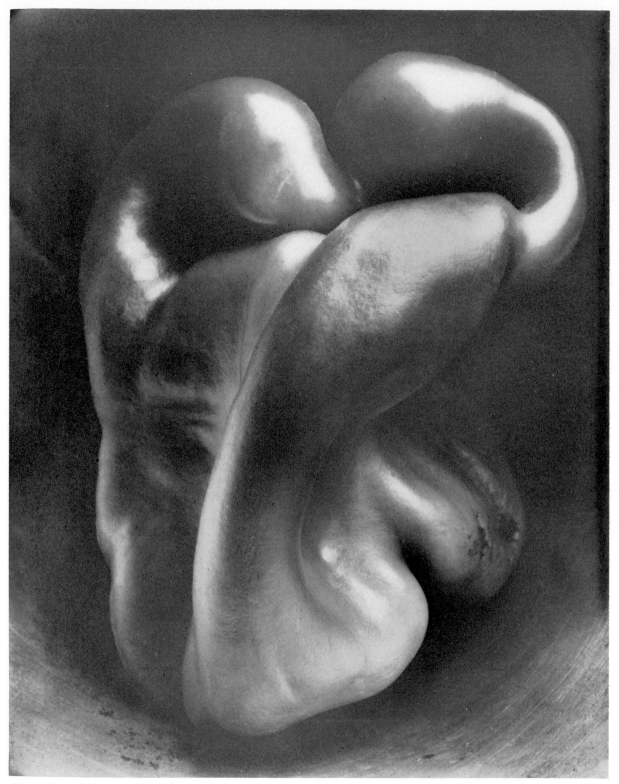

44. **Edward Weston.** Paprica. 1930.

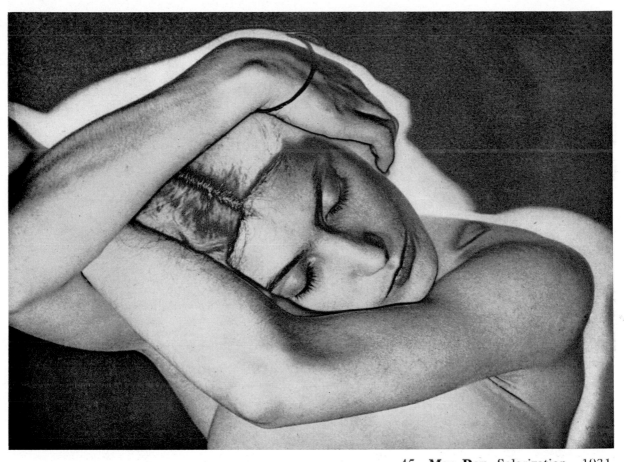

45. **Man Ray.** Solarization. 1931.

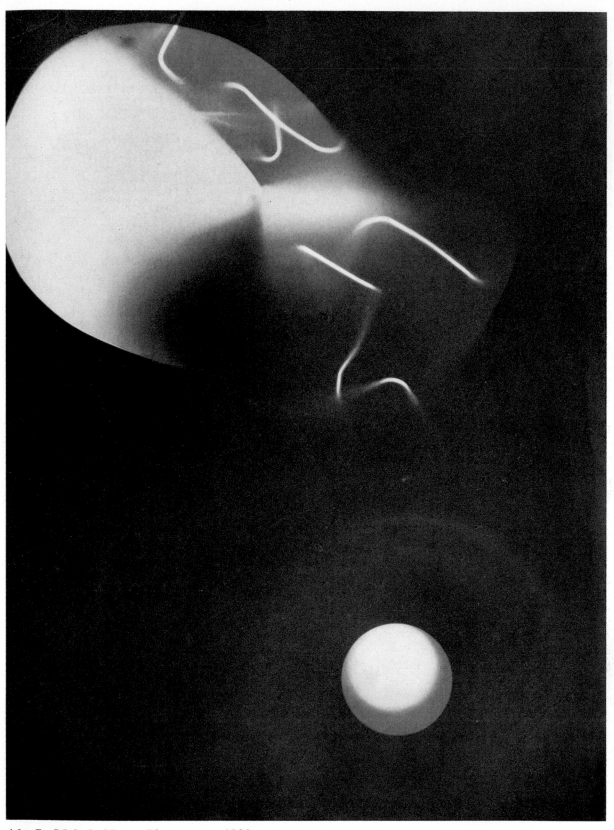

46. **L. Moholy-Nagy.** Photogram. 1922.

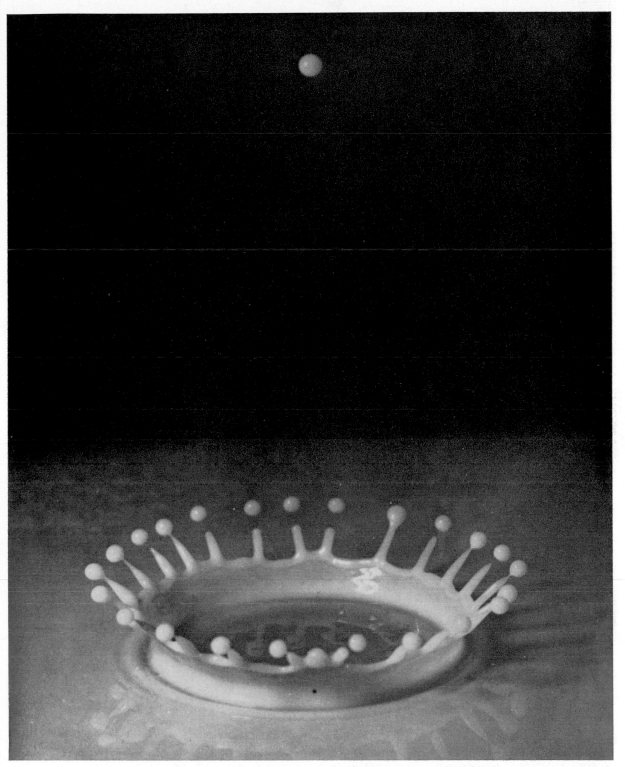

47. **Harold E. Edgerton.** Splash of milk resulting from a drop of milk. 1936.

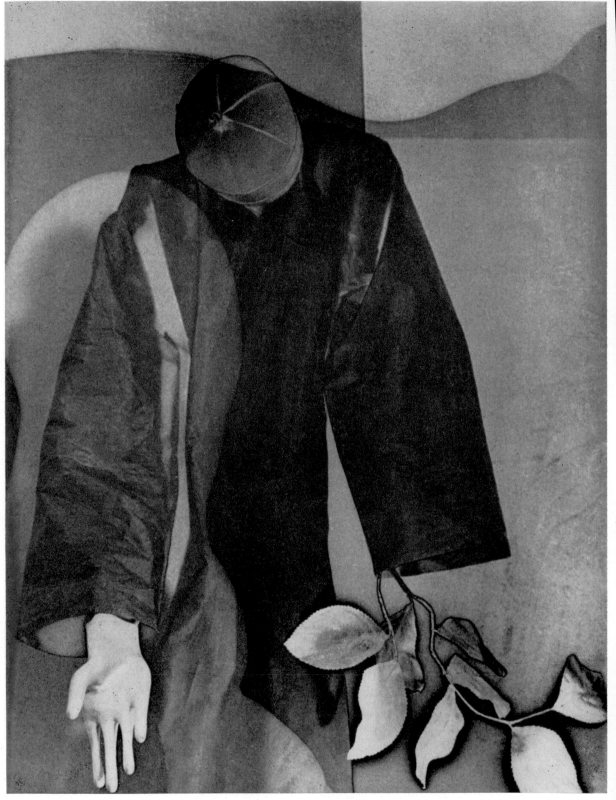

48. **Winifred Casson.** Surrealist composition. c. 1935.

KING-SMITH-EVANS-WINTER-HEBB CO., DETROIT, LETTERPRESS U.S.A